ARC ROAD

The Horrific Murders of Three Police Officers
in Gwinnett County Georgia
That Changed Law Enforcement Forever

Tony Tiffin

Genius
Book Publishing

Los Angeles, California

Published By:
Genius Book Publishing
31858 Castaic Road, #154
Castaic, CA 91384
GeniusBookPublishing.com

ISBN: 978-1-947521-10-0
Library of Congress Control Number: 2019947536

190826

TABLE OF CONTENTS

AUTHOR'S NOTE

All of the dialog, including the thoughts and feelings of individuals in the moments described, is taken from court transcripts and interviews with the individuals to whom they are attributed. Some liberties were taken with the exact wording, but the sentiment expressed is as close to their actual words and thoughts as was reasonably attainable.

Also, while all of the important individuals named in this book are real and did the things mentioned within these pages, a few otherwise nameless men and women who had minor roles in these events are composites of the actual people involved and given names to avoid the awkwardness of leaving them anonymous. Any inaccuracies, on this front and elsewhere in theses pages, are my own.

ACKNOWLEDGMENTS

This book is the product of a combination of sources, from court transcripts and official records to personal recollections of those who were there. I received help from family members, law enforcement officials, and other experts in the field of forensics, as well as the good townspeople of Duluth, Suwanee, Sugar Hill, and Buford, Georgia, without whom I would have nothing but a collection of conjecture and speculation. I thank each and every person who helped me, but in order to avoid a lengthy roll call I will privately remember all with my sincerest gratitude.

Arc Road is not my story. It belongs to Gwinnett County, Georgia, and to all those who lived through this terrible event. I appreciate all the help you have given me in bringing this story back into current memory. I could never be more indebted.

To Jennie

ARC ROAD

PROLOGUE

Guthrie Farm spread over a two mile stretch of rolling woods and pasture. Through its heart coursed a narrow tree-lined lane of dirt named Arc Road.

Tall pines and hardwoods stood thick on the road's west border. At the sun's high point almost no light penetrated the lush tree canopy.

At night open fields on the east side of the road glowed silver as dew-covered pastures reflected the light of the moon and stars.

Only a very few people had ever heard of Arc Road, but by noon on April 17, 1964 it was the obsession of everybody in the county. A day later, the whole world would know the name.

Gwinnett County, Georgia, 430 square miles of chicken farms, cotton fields and dirt roads, neither sought nor wanted the notoriety. The county in those days was still the Old South, where daily routines hadn't much changed in a hundred years. Monday through Saturday was for work and chores. Sunday was for church and family. People led a country lifestyle in a place and time when folks had what they needed and didn't desire much more. The life was hardscrabble to some; it was God's way to most others.

In its early days, Gwinnett was just a handful of little settlements that had sprung up along the Chattahoochee River. By the 1960s, they'd grown into towns along the Southern Railroad that ran north out of Atlanta. From Doraville, on the county's south line, the rail ran through Norcross and on to Duluth. From Duluth, it continued to Suwanee, Sugar Hill, and finally, on the northern line, the city of Buford. The train carried mostly freight, but during fall harvest, mostly cotton. Five hundred pound bales stacked high atop countless flat cars. On either side of the track between towns there wasn't a lot to see other than pastures. It took more than a quick look to find evidence of humanity.

In addition to the railroad, Gwinnett had two-lane paved roads that joined most towns, and the new Northeast Expressway split the county in half, making it a whole lot easier to get around and go pretty much wherever you wanted.

U.S. Highway 23 was the main road in the western part of the county, which ran alongside the railroad track from Atlanta all the way to Buford. For the first few miles the road was called Buford Highway. Past Norcross, folks just called it Twenty-three. Ask for directions and you were likely to hear, "Go up to Twenty-three, then turn in the direction you want to go." One could only go north or south. If you went anywhere farther beyond the tracks, even locals would likely be lost.

Between the towns U.S. 23 went through, it was an empty country road. Every few miles, scattered about in the hills, sat what were called shotgun houses. These tin-roofed wood structures usually had two bedrooms, a main room, a kitchen, and always a front porch. Mama and Daddy and small babies slept in one bedroom, older kids in the other. Visitors had to make themselves comfortable wherever.

Water came from a community well pumped to a spigot in the front yard. A lucky few had a spigot inside. Luckier still were the families with one in the kitchen. In the country, you lived by one simple rule: if you wanted food on your table, you either had to grow it or slaughter it. In the backyard, residents plowed an acre or so of what folks called red Georgia clay and turned it into a vegetable garden where beans, corn, okra, and tomatoes grew. Everybody had chickens that roamed about the yard, mostly free. There was no need for a pen, as chickens generally don't go far.

The South provided a long growing season for producing fresh vegetables. Folks usually had plenty left over for canning or pickling to get through the winter. Some grew extra for truck farming and sharing, especially with those no longer able to tend their own gardens or raise animals.

The people of the area were, to outsiders' standards, poor, but in the country food was as good as money. You could trade food for most anything. During growing season, you could take fresh vegetables to the general store and trade them for salt, sugar, or other necessary staples. One chicken would get you an ice-cold Coca-Cola, a bag of candy, and a pack of cigarettes.

Suwanee had a school building that housed grades one through twelve. School wasn't a requirement, and for a fact, many boys never finished. After learning basic reading and writing, they'd drop out, taking jobs on local farms to make a few dollars their families desperately needed. In those days, a strong back was worth more than a strong mind. The thinking of country folks was hard work taught a boy common sense he'd never get from any schoolhouse.

Truth be told, folks in Suwanee didn't live any different than most everybody else in Gwinnett County and probably all of North Georgia. You could say it was right peaceful as folks lived a pure life driven by the "Holy Scripture." But all that would soon change.

The new Northeast Expressway was a seventy-five-mile-an-hour dragstrip straight into downtown Atlanta. Took less than thirty minutes getting to where clean, Monday through Friday jobs were. All of a sudden, Gwinnett boys could make more money per day down there than they could in a week of scratching potatoes out of some farmer's dirt field. With their newfound riches, they were buying cars, houses, and console televisions, and raising families in neighborhoods their parents could have only dreamed of.

And those country boys weren't going back, not to a homestead and not to dirt fields.

എ

Near the crossroads of downtown Buford, Georgia, there was a small country cafeteria where cozy booths lined three interior walls. The patrons reflected the quaintness of traditional southern values in both dress and manners. They exchanged soft smiles and poignant anecdotes of former days living in rural north Georgia. It was the high space of those interior walls that held my attention, though, for they portrayed through enlarged faded photographs the story of early Gwinnett County law enforcement: sheriffs, police chiefs, and hard-nosed cops, the restaurant proprietor himself having been in law enforcement for two decades. Although the men in those pictures of fifty years past may have lost their slender, youthful appearance, little had diminished their recollection of lawless behavior or the disgust from half a century before when three of their close police officer friends were viciously murdered on a forgotten dirt road not ten miles east of the café's now barren walls.

On many occasions I had the honor of listening as Arnold, Dan, Edwin, Fred, George, Larry, Roger, and others, most notably Robert Hightower, recounted the black-and-white images of that time. In exchange I felt an obligation to provide meaning for what occurred and memorialize those brave Gwinnett County patrolmen who perished one April night long ago.

A journey for lost history of fifty years earlier represented a long road. A road that had to be traveled to find old memories through doors that had to be opened. It required not only diligence but a good amount of luck. I got lucky and entered musty attics, rustled through dark closets, and pried open closed chests. I walked among the best in law enforcement and through the dread of prison hallways. I often annoyed court recorders, irritated salvage yard operators, and fearfully admired the brilliance of medical examiners. I found critical autopsy reports, articles of clothing, missing guns, a stray bullet and, of all things cherished, two cigars and a book of matches inside an old motorcycle boot. The journey allowed me to meet the most amazing people in my lifetime, a reward in itself well worth the trip.

This isn't a story that affected someone else, somewhere else. I lived in Gwinnett County in 1964. However, this story is not my story. It belongs to those who lived and cried through it as it happened. I only convey it; it is they who tell it, those amazing people and their amazing story. Here now, I share it for them.

THE LAW

Southern folks can be set fast in their ways. In the 1960s folks in Gwinnett County were prime examples of this. There were just certain things we preferred best left alone, the law being one; law enforcement, to be clear. Not that we were opposed to it. Several towns in the county had a police department of its very own: usually a chief and one or two officers, all that was needed.

In the early 1960s law enforcement in Gwinnett County was "maybe reactive." Make a phone call and maybe you would get a response. Folks reported simple stuff mostly: a car off in a ditch, neighbors fussing over fence rights, a stubborn cow out loose blocking the road. Police got called to come nudge it back home. Used a gentle tap with the car bumper for persuasion.

For the whole of Gwinnett we elected a sheriff. As a matter of fact, Gwinnett had two sheriffs, the only county in Georgia that did. The Sugar Hill district had a sheriff who worked civil or misdemeanor cases, and the Lawrenceville district had what we called the high sheriff, who worked more serious crimes, such as felonies. Both courts had their own solicitors who had their own investigators. With two sheriffs and all those city police, we figured there was enough law to go around, but our elected commissioners, who took joy in ruling over us, figured otherwise. They wanted a county police department able to coordinate with city police but to remain separate from the sheriff's department.

At the time there was good reason for an independent department, so we took to the idea as long as the commissioners understood that we needed policing only as much as we wanted policing, and no more. It soon turned out they were right about this police thing. Give them all the credit. See, a short time earlier we'd put ourselves in one hell of a fix. We didn't know it at the time, though. Nonetheless, it was our own fault for letting it happen.

For years we'd been told by local candidates that if elected, they'd sweep out all the illegal stills in the county. As far as stills were concerned, didn't hardly anybody see any wrong in it. Nobody was getting hurt by it. Finally, enough was heard of politicians' empty promises to where we figured up a way in stopping all this talk. Come Election Day, we voted into office, as our new high sheriff, a man who just happened to be the biggest still owner in the county. Convenient, but brother, let me tell you, it was a big mistake! The order of law quickly changed. He turned our county jailhouse into the headquarters for his own personal business empire. County prisoners became county employees. By day they'd bring in supplies for making his mash, and by moonlight they hauled the finished product to distributors down in Atlanta. Between shifts he gave them room and board at the jailhouse. They could come and go as they pleased. To make matters worse, the whole operation was supervised by two of his deputies. They formed a posse to raid small stills, but instead of using a pickaxe to destroy the workings they used a pipe wrench to take them apart and haul them off. Now you best believe those stills didn't end up as no water trough on no chicken farm.

Several deputies who at first were not involved complained to the sheriff, "Your prisoners are making more money than we are. What about us getting a pay raise?"

The sheriff replied, "Boys, the county ain't got no money for pay raises, but you can get all you want out there on them roads." Shortly thereafter speed traps began springing up across the county. Whenever someone got pulled over, they'd have two choices: either pay a cash fine to the deputy or go to jail. For moonshiners, deputies set up check points, or rather toll roads, charging ten dollars for protected passage. Moonshining was a dangerous business. Drivers were vulnerable to hijackers who'd take their load and car both. Protection was worth the money. No need for liquor haulers fearing the law. Lawmen were a known commodity. It was the unknown that moonshiners feared. There ain't no telling what might happen running those roads at night. Lots of bad stuff creeps about on them dirt roads. Never know who or what you'll be messing with.

This one fella, good guy, didn't know the ropes. Had no idea what he was getting into. Decided one day he was going to build for himself a liquor car. Took a couple of months to do and everybody knew what he was doing. Wasn't no secret about it. His first run turned out to be his last. Got hijacked, very first night. Bad guys saw him coming, blocked his way, pulled him from the driver's seat, beat the crap out of him, and kicked him into the ditch. Fella said he looked up and saw two shadowy figures staring down at him from the road.

One told him, "This will be your only warning. Don't come running these roads no more. If we catch you out here again, gonna be a whole lots worse."

They took his car, took his liquor, and took his money too. Left him there in the mud, covered all up in stink, wondering what in the hell just happened.

The following morning, the guy goes complaining to the sheriff. "Look what they done to me, and you know who it was. Robbed me of my new car, all my damn money, and beat me near to death. Sheriff, I wanna bring charges against them boys."

"Uh-huh."

"Dang it all, Sheriff, I ain't just kidding! Look here what they done to me! Now you go out there and get 'em."

Big old sheriff grabbed this fella by his shirt collar, walked him to the jail cell, and threw him in, slamming the door shut behind. Sheriff told him, "Found your car this morning. Was sitting up near Highway Twenty-three, right where you left it last night, plum out of gas. Oh, you was hauling liquor, all right. Didn't have none in it, but I could sure smell it. Got yourself all fallen down drunk walking your way back home. That's how I see it, and that's how I'm gonna write it. Now you're gonna sit here in this cell all quiet like for ten days charged with unlawful distribution of distilled liquor. Against the law running white liquor, or didn't you know? Ten days ought to teach you better."

It did. That was the boy's first and last day in the liquor business.

Although Gwinnett was a dry county, "associates" of the sheriff opened bars in their homes, sold liquor by the drink, and called them shot houses. One night a group of men hijacked a trailer loaded with bonded red liquor out of Kentucky. Stole it from a secured truck yard off the Northeast Expressway. The sheriff knew those boys, and don't you know, he confiscated that liquor. Told them to keep close mouthed or else. His "or else," by the way, was not a pretty thing. He took the confiscations and stored them in an outbuilding behind the jailhouse. It didn't stay stored long. He sold it, a case at a time, to his network of shot houses. Made himself real good money.

Everybody knew about the gambling parlors that ran around the clock, seven days a week. Long as they tidied up with the sheriff, there'd be no problems. Before long the sheriff's enterprise was making money coming and going. Didn't take us long to realize the county was wide open for every crook and every drunk who'd never given one thought of getting through the day sober. If a city police chief was to express concern about all these improprieties, the sheriff would fire him. Was two that did and were! As time went on, we no longer knew who to trust. Couldn't tell the good guys from the bad.

The county was in such a way to where it seemed a lost cause, but fortunately this was not a fact lost on the commissioners. Our sheriff had positioned himself as the boss of law enforcement in Gwinnett, but every boss has a boss. In his case it was the Georgia Bureau of Investigation (GBI). The State Patrol was the uniform division of the GBI, and it had, along with the FBI, plenty enough muscle to bring the sheriff down. It began to unravel when a straight-laced deputy, gone all this while to Army Reserve camp, came home to resume his duties. On his first day back at the jailhouse, he took one look inside and couldn't believe the sight. A half dozen men were sleeping inside the cells with doors open, muddy boots thrown on the floor, dirty overalls hanging off the cell bars, and right there in plain sight, a jar of white liquor next to a man's bunk.

He stormed into the sheriff's office hollering, "What in the world is going on around here?"

The sheriff shouted back, "Calm down. Don't you worry yourself about it."

The deputy yelled back, "Don't worry about it my ass! Somebody around here is going to federal prison, and it sure ain't gonna be me. You can take that right here and now as my resignation." He stomped out of that jailhouse never to look back.

That night the police commissioner drove out to the deputy's house asking why he'd resigned. The former deputy told him what he'd seen earlier and heard since, said he wanted no part of it.

Not surprised by the deputy's story but impressed with his nerve against the sheriff, the commissioner offered him a job as his new investigator. Smart move. Turned out the deputy was indeed right about what he'd warned the sheriff.

Took a while to get everybody in proper step, but once together, the Feds finally sealed the lid on that guy. The stolen load of bonded red liquor out of Kentucky gave the Feds authority to get involved. An FBI agent posing as a buyer for one of the local shot houses bought two cases of the seized liquor from a deputy. GBI agents staked out surveillance positions along the only trail leading to the sheriff's still operation. High-speed infrared cameras filmed two of his deputies directing the night-time operation. Some of his mash made its way over state lines, which brought in the Bureau of Alcohol, Tobacco and Firearms, and the Georgia Department of Revenue came in with tax evasion.

Finally enough evidence had been gathered to put that bunch in front of a judge. That was a good day! Was an even better day watching U.S. Marshals cart our high sheriff and one of his deputies off to federal prison. But the county had not rid themselves of that deputy. Not by a long shot.

Not long afterwards our commissioners made an interim appointment to fulfill the old sheriff's term, but—lesson learned—they stripped the sheriff's department of all arresting powers. In a request granted by the Georgia Bureau of Investigation, the state patrol temporarily assumed all law enforcement duties for Gwinnett until our new county police department got up and running.

The Police Commissioner's first order of business was finding someone with leadership experience to head up the department. Already in his mind was the perfect man for the job, J. O. Bell, a close friend the commissioner had grown up with in the county. Mr. Bell had recently retired as a chief petty officer in the United States Navy after thirty years. You couldn't find a better man in Gwinnett for "by the book" protocol, but it was Bell's naval experience in organizing a loose group of men into a tight knit team that made him the ideal choice. Without a doubt he had all the qualities for making a fine police chief. All except for one. He had no law enforcement experience, so it wasn't exactly like he came crawling to town begging for the job. No, J. O. had retired and was perfectly content tending his backyard garden.

Finding Bell where he was at his leisure, the police commissioner paid him a surprise visit. "Figured I'd catch you dirty handed, J. O. Sure couldn't have picked a finer day, huh?"

Bell, kneeling in the dirt, said, "How about you watch where you put your big damn feet? Them's my tomato plants you're standing on."

"Oh yeah, I see that I am. Well, I'm sorry. Guess you're looking at the biggest lug you ever did see."

Bell nodded in disagreement, "Nope, seen this one other."

Feeling already the awkward intruder, the commissioner began, "This probably isn't the best time to ask –"

"Yeah, probably right"

"Gonna ask anyway. Didn't come all the way out here not to. Besides, I thought you were a body who loves a challenge. If my thinking is right, then you're fixing to hear some good news."

Bell raised his head. "Only good news I wanna hear is the sound of your car leaving."

"Okay, you old salt dog, listen here. You've heard we're starting a county police department?"

"Yeah, well, best of luck with that."

"Oh, we're gonna have real good luck with that. You can bet on it. Look here what I brung with me."

The commissioner reached into his coat pocket and pulled out his closed hand. He held it in front of Bell then slowly opened his fingers, "This is what I come here to show you." Glistening in the sunlight was a gold-over-chrome badge embossed Gwinnett County Police. Its black enamel center read in bold letters the title Chief.

Bell let out a slight groan as he stood. He stared in quiet awe at the majestic shield shining in front of him. To J. O. it defined the county he loved and would defend with all his being. He said nothing as he reached out, taking the badge from the commissioner's hand. He quietly read the embossment and realized the reason for the commissioner's visit and his words about challenge. He found himself taken by emotion for his adored Gwinnett. Holding the badge in his right palm he gently rubbed its lettering. He glared into the commissioner's eyes, "You son of a bitch! You know good and damn well I'm gonna keep this badge. Gonna wear it too! Plenty here in this county have hell to pay. Don't mind that I help see they pay it."

The relieved commissioner said, "You know it, Chief! Damn sure do! Let me show you your new office in the morning. Meet me at the jailhouse say around eight o'clock thereabouts."

Bell, always military punctual, responded, "Nope! You be there sharp!"

J. O. didn't flinch when he took the badge from the commissioner's hand, but the commissioner did. He understood what Bell meant when he said there'd be hell to pay.

J. O. understood all too well what the commissioner meant about challenge, that little matter about not having any law enforcement experience. What he needed was someone who did. Someone he could trust, who had a reputation in Gwinnett as a hard-nosed city cop that didn't take crap from nobody. J. O. knew the perfect man for the job. M. J. Puckett, a twenty-year veteran in county law enforcement was an officer who took police work serious, and anyone who stepped over the line quickly learned how serious he was.

That night Chief Bell drove to Puckett's house. The burly policeman was sitting inside his living room. Without knocking Bell opened the front screen door and barged in. "Look alive, Puckett! This ain't no time to be sleeping"

Puckett, not surprised, said, "Didn't them Navy bastards never teach you no manners on that tugboat of yours? Come busting in here all high and mighty like."

"You're damn right about that. I am all high and mighty." Bell pulled the badge out from his pants pocket, "You ever learn how to read? Well, get an eye load of this."

Puckett stared dumbfounded at the badge, "What the damned hell?"

"You've heard talk they're putting together a County Police Department? Well, mister, it ain't talk no more! They's doing it! Sons of bitches made me Chief of Police, and I'm the son of a bitch who's making you my right-hand man. How's Assistant Chief sound? Now before answering, let me tell you what I have in mind. I'll manage it and do all the paperwork. You'll command it and do all the ass kicking. You'll have everything you need to do the job. Just ask and it's yours. Let me take care of the commissioners. Course they'll wanna rope a ring through our noses, try and pull us whichever way they want, but I ain't gonna have none of that. Gonna be done our way, I'm here to tell ya. First thing I'll do is get us a couple of patrol cars. You get us two of the toughest cops you can find to put in em."

"Shit! What do you know about police work?" Puckett shook his head while pointing at Bell. "Now before answering, let me tell you! You don't know a goddamn thing about police work."

"Well hell, Puckett, I know that. But I guess you didn't hear what I said. You're gonna be my Assistant Chief. Everybody knows that's who makes it work. Besides, ain't nobody else I believe can. Prove me I'm right."

Puckett nodded, "Bullshit! I ain't gotta prove nothing!"

Bell turned his back. The fear of rejection stole his hope. M. J. was a tough cop, but this was a tough county. The proposition of starting a new department from scratch wasn't all that appealing to him. The risks far outweighed the rewards. Police work was not a game played by amateurs. The slightest situation could quickly blow up into an unthinkable consequence.

Bell took a deep breath and then turned around, facing Puckett, "Will you at least give it some thought? Please!?" He looked down at the floor while nodding his head. "Damn it M. J., you can say no if you want, and I ain't gonna hold it against you but, just know this: I can't do it without you."

"Uh-huh."

Bell made one last plea. "Here's your chance—our chance. We can finally get this goddamn county straight, something we've both said it needs many a time."

Puckett admired and respected J. O. Bell more than any other man. They had been close friends for years. Puckett didn't need to give much thought to Bell's request. Slowly gazing up and then down at his discouraged friend, he said, "Well now, look at you. Chief of Police, huh? Hell, you ain't no lawman. Never wore a badge in your life. Got no idea." Puckett continued staring at his desperate ally. "Got no damn idea whatsoever. Oh well, to hell with us all! You're goddamn right I'll do it. Gonna have to, to keep your ass out of trouble, paper boy." Puckett stared with pride at his old friend. "Tell me when and where."

Puckett's acceptance brought Bell to crow, "We're gonna hit it first thing in the morning, full on. I'll come get you at seven thirty sharp. Have yourself on ready." Smiling wide, Bell turned quickly toward the front door to leave before Puckett had a change of mind. "Don't get your ass up for me I can find my own way out." After stepping off the front porch and walking back to his car, Bell looked over his shoulder. "Oh, by the way, Mr. Puckett, y'all have a good evening."

Puckett yelled, "Yeah, do the same, Mr. Police Chief. God help us!"

A mutual bond had teamed these old friends together for a cause both believed in, but both knew the joking would stop in the morning. Together they would have to restore county folks' belief that the law worked for them. Gwinnett had no shortage of boys who not once in their miserable lives ever sat in a church pew, boys with nothing better to do than make trouble, especially when they took to drinking. Puckett knew who they were and had probably thrown each of them in jail at some time. He also knew most everything that went on in the county, law abiding or not.

Puckett had his own approach to police work, "Get there firstist with the mostist, be it the easy way or be it the hard way." The hard way a body wouldn't soon forget. To wear a badge under Puckett's command you had to be a special breed -- tough. Anything you got yourself into you had to get yourself out of. There was no backup.

After twenty years of policing, Puckett had by that time patrolled with every cop in the county. Filling Chief Bell's order for two of the toughest wasn't a problem. Working for the City Police of Duluth was a young officer who shared Puckett's ideas of law enforcement. Jerry Everett came into this world forged of iron from a blast furnace, a blue cat you best not cross paths with. If Officer Everett told you to do something, let there be no hesitation; he wasn't gonna tell you twice. A body thinking otherwise would soon find himself on the ground praying for God's mercy. One day a well-known boy from the county, a nasty punk full of piss and vinegar, learned this lesson the hard way.

Everett responded to a disorderly conduct call finding the hopped-up punk approaching him with the wrong look on his face and the wrong words coming out his mouth. "Well, what have we got here? Big bad policeman come to take me away? You a dumb cop fixing to get yourself a good ass whopping."

Everett, not at all intimidated, told the boy, "Shut that mouth and take your hands out of your pockets!"

"You don't tell me what to do! I'll take my hands out whenever the hell I want to."

Everett walked up to the boy and slapped his face so hard that the loud mouth's left eyeball popped out of its socket. Came clean out the socket! Jerry drove him to Joan Glancy Hospital while the boy sat quietly in the patrol car's backseat holding his eye against his face.

Later that night Officer Everett drove back to the hospital for a quick visit.

The boy's eye had been repaired and his attitude adjusted. "Mister, why did you have to hit me like that?"

Everett stood looking down at him. "Boy, you just learned a valuable lesson today. The next time a police officer tells you to remove your hands from your pockets, what are you gonna do?"

The punk rolled over on the pillow and took to crying.

Officer Everett quietly left the room, no further dialogue needed.

The second cop Puckett hired was a veteran police officer from the city of Lawrenceville, Leonard Bowen. Folks called him Mr. Bowen, but close friends called him by his nickname, Bull. Now you sure better believe it's best not to mess with a Gwinnett cop that goes by the name Bull. Mr. Bowen was the end all for any problems caused by hotshot troublemakers. One Friday night during a square dance at the American Legion Hall in Duluth this ornery fella, mean as a hungry black bear who'd beat the daylights out of no telling how many, came drunk looking for a fight. He found several.

Mr. Bowen, relaxing at home, got a phone call to go resolve the problem. There were already a few officers in the parking lot when Bull pulled in. He got out of his car, walked up, grabbed this fella by his shirt collar and told him, "Get in the back of that officer's car! You're drunk, and you're gonna sleep it off in jail."

The fella says to Bowen, "Get your damn hands off me."

Bowen held his blackjack high. "I said get in that officer's patrol car right now, or I'll bust that dumb ass brain of yours out of them deaf ears."

After the man got in the patrol car, Bull leaned through the window and gave a warning. "Don't make me have to come up here and deal with your sorry ass again. You hear me, boy? Not one more time!"

On the way to jail the guy asked the officer driving, "Can that big son of a bitch talk to me like that?"

The policeman turned facing him. "Well yeah, and you might ought to do what Mr. Bowen tells you to do or else he's gonna show you what he says."

Some people just don't listen, and this fella wasn't gonna take any advice from no cop. Sure enough, the very next Friday night, he came back drunk again, picking a fight. Well, after getting called, here comes Mr. Bowen again, pulling into the parking lot. He walked up to this fella without saying a word, pulled out his blackjack, and framed the top of that boy's head. Made a mess of him. It took four officers to load him into the patrol car.

A few days later, after the fella regained what little sense he ever had, Officer Bowen paid him a visit in the hospital. Standing at his bedside he held up his blackjack, waved it in front of the man's face. "Sure did have a good time at the Legion Hall last Friday night. Let me know when you want to do it again, hear?" The old cop left the room leaving this guy shivering in his bed.

A few days after his appointment, Puckett said to Chief Bell, "I hired them two officers you told me to get."

"Are they any good?"

Puckett launched into a wide-eyed grin, nodding. "Well, let me put it to you like this: if we have a warrant needs serving on the Devil, them two boys will go to Hell in the hereafter, get him, and bring him back. Him or his pitchfork, one."

Chief Bell grimaced.

Puckett didn't exaggerate about his cops. There weren't going to be no choir boys on his force. He expected his officers to be pig-iron tough, and that they were, but he also demanded they have absolute integrity. All that stuff about serve and protect meant nothing without integrity. In Puckett's way of thinking, that's what the badge stood for.

A police officer's job is out mingling with the people, being a friend folks could trust. Everett and Bowen had a tight handle on that. Both were nice guys, as good as you'd ever meet. Helping folks was part of their makeup. Could be a stalled car had a boiled-over radiator needed water or somebody's pet went missing and needed finding. Many days a cop used his lug wrench for changing a flat tire more than his booklet for writing a ticket. This kind of policing wasn't beneath them, but actually preferred. Cops don't mind a little grease on their hands. Sure beats the alternative.

Hired from pure luck, Puckett's third man was another experienced police officer, John Paul Harris. Harris also came from the Lawrenceville department and, like Chief Bell, was a former Navy seaman. He had a solid moral character and in uniform carried no other concern than doing good police work. Harris was a straight-laced career-minded officer with no excuses, always a safety first kind of guy. He played it to his advantage as a happy-go-lucky fella. Wasn't anything wrong with Harris if someone wanted to have a little "country boy" fun. But if the "country boy" turned to trouble, Mr. Harris turned with him. Fun over!

In a short time the county had earned back a trust with Gwinnett folks and they showed their appreciation at the polling booth. A few months later the commissioner gave Chief Bell the okay for more officers. Puckett hired his old friend Quinton Roberts, a police officer he'd patrolled with many times. Strangers called him Mr. Roberts, but friends called him Jake. He wasn't much over five feet tall in his boots. Would've been taller with his hat on, but Jake never wore his police hat. He claimed wearing that hat made him look like a rabbit under a fig leaf. Among his police friends the nickname Rabbit stuck. That wasn't no slight on Jake. A wild rabbit can outrun an outlaw, chase him down quick and chew his ass a new one. Roberts ran to trouble, not away from it, a quality Puckett required in all his officers, hat or no hat.

As the sheriff's office was busted of all arresting powers, the new county department became Gwinnett's sole law enforcers. With only two patrol cars and four officers, this deal wasn't cutting it—too many dirt roads, too many double shifts. Hard pressed to expand, Bell asked the Commissioner for additional funds.

"No! I've given you all I can." The Commissioner pointed out the window. "We got a big old county out there, in case you haven't noticed. Everybody needs more money. Only way you get yours is if I take theirs, and that ain't gonna happen."

Not one to mince his words, Bell held firm to the promise he made Puckett. "I didn't come here for nothing. I accepted your shit-grinning offer for this job and along with it the responsibility of upholding the law for the good folks of this big old stinking county. Hell, man, I came out of retirement for you. If I don't get what I need, you best find yourself a new chief!" Bell pointed out the window, "I ain't gonna send them boys out there one more day the way things are now. I'm going back to my garden, and you can be chief for all I care."

The Commissioner reeled. "Okay, okay, you're right! Ain't you always? But I never said it would be easy. Listen, you've brought your department a long ways, I'm pleased to say. Wish I could say that about the others. All right, let me see what I can do. Give me a couple days, will you?"

Bell, ever impatient said, "A couple days?"

"Well hell, man, it's not like I print the stuff in the back room. Yeah, a couple days, and if you knew better, you'd know that ain't asking much."

"All right, you got it. A couple of days. I'll be expecting you."

The commissioner began borrowing, hustling, and downright stealing every dollar he could get his hands on. Two nights later he drove to Bell's house. With his grin gone, he firmly told Bell, "Beginning tomorrow you have my permission to double your force and buy two more patrol cars, but here's the deal. The officers will be paid two hundred dollars a month. No insurance, no pension. They'll have to buy their own uniforms, their own hats, their own boots, belts, guns, and holsters. They'll even have to buy their own bullets. That's the best I can do."

Chief Bell thought on it for a moment. "I'm not gonna find any experienced officers to work under those conditions."

"I'm sure you're right, but I've done my part, now you'll just have to do yours. Take it or leave it."

Bell took the deal but worried his assistant chief might not. He went to Puckett and relayed the information.

Puckett said, "Oh good lord, they're all gonna be green as turnips. Gotta buy their own bullets? Shit, who's that bastard think he's kidding?" Puckett quickly saw Bell's wits were at their frayed end with worry. He was purely concerned the low budget could be the end of the new department. It had happened before. His timbre changed, "Hey, Mr. Police Chief, ease your mind. You ain't got no need fretting over this. I'll get us some boys. Get them bullets too. Lots of bullets! Don't worry about that, don't worry about nothing! Hell, we done this to start. Get those two cars, and I'll train us up some of the best goddamn cops you ever did see"

Relieved his assistant chief was in command, Bell exhaled a long deep breath. "Puckett, I can't tell you how much I —"

"No, you can't. Least not right now. But give me a little time, I'll figure you a way."

After completing a no-background-check application there were but two requirements the new police hires had to meet: walk upright and have a pulse. Even so, when considering the pay and benefits the job offered, those requirements did seem a might harsh. The pay was extremely low and there were no benefits, and because the recruit had to buy all his own gear, the line that formed in response to Puckett's Help Wanted sign was a short one. Essentially there was no line. Nobody showed. Puckett had to first find and then sell his open positions to "free-spirited men who held a desire for adventure," a sales job the Fuller Brush man himself couldn't have done, but it worked.

The first of the new hires was Ray Sexton. Puckett lured Sexton from behind the counter of a small general store up Buford way. Sexton knew a lot of folks up there and had a reputation of treating them fairly, another one of the traits Puckett demanded. The saying about Sexton was he'd give a needy man the shirt off his back. He was an honorable man, having not one crooked bone in his body. Of particular note, Sexton drove a car like no one else. Could do a bootlegger's spin, where a fella would hang a gear and head back in the opposite direction without the speedometer needle dropping. There were a few ol' boys in the county who had the touch, but Ray Sexton could do it under a railroad bridge.

The commissioner himself submitted a distant kin for Puckett's next recruit. Ralph Davis came from Gwinnett's northernmost stretch. He'd grown up a humble farm boy. While working in a corn field one day, his daddy dropped dead of a heart attack, leaving behind nothing for the family but debt and a few farm tools. Ralph and his brother Clyde had spent an entire year scrubbing up field dirt to repay that debt. That's just the way country folks do. When all was settled, the brothers split less than a dollar between them. Ralph Davis was a quiet man with a reputation as the guy you'd call if you were to throw a party that needed a body to stand against the wall. He'd not bother a soul but, like wasps, poke on the nest or poke on Ralph, and you're gonna get stung.

One morning a group of rednecks had surrounded Ralph on the porch of a general store. One of the boys pulled out a knife and challenged him to a fight. Ralph said he didn't carry a knife, so one was thrown down at his feet as the attacker lunged. Ralph took a cut to his arm but stuck that thrown knife square in the boy's chest, and within minutes the big punk bled out. At his trial several witnesses vouched for Ralph saying it was self-defense, but the judge said it was manslaughter and sentenced him to five years hard labor on a Georgia chain gang.

Twenty years had passed since his parole, and although he was well known for his past, no ill feelings were ever held against him. In fact Ralph Davis was admired and respected for his moral character. He took great pride in being a police officer, and the department was proud to have him as one of their own.

Carl Gravitt drove out to the jailhouse and applied for the last open position. His older brother, Jesse, went along for the ride. Carl had law enforcement experience as a security guard for Lockheed Aircraft in Marietta, Georgia. He had always wanted to be a police officer. Jesse, on the other hand, never gave it the least thought but filled out an application anyway. Why not? A few days later Puckett read Carl Gravitt's resume and liked what he saw, so ain't it ever a wonder that somehow the brothers' names got flipped, and Jesse got the call, Marvin Jesse Gravitt in full. Friends just called him Jess, and young cops called him Pops because ol' Jess gave out advice could only a daddy give. He took no offense from being called Pops as long as it came from a cop. All others respectfully called him Mr. Gravitt. Jesse was a real man, able to shoe horses, hitch a mule team, and plant a farm. Knew his way around heavy machinery too. Had a keen mind full-up with common sense. Chief Bell figured that after a few years of police work Jesse would go on to a higher calling in the county, probably a civil servant or maybe even be a commissioner.

Including Assistant Chief Puckett, the department now had eight officers patrolling in four squad cars. Puckett rode with the new officers for their first few months until he was satisfied they could handle it themselves. From then on they were paired with experienced cops. Dividing the county into quarters, each car patrolled a specific zone. Officer Sexton drove for either Bell or Puckett, alternating between mornings and afternoons. On occasion they'd drive the whole county but normally patrolled only the north quarter. Roberts and Harris patrolled the east section during the afternoon. Gravitt and Bowen covered the south side on the night shift. Davis rode with Everett patrolling the west side. Each shift overlapped the next so at least one car would be on patrol early morning till late night providing police service for the county near twenty hours a day. Between three and six AM, only chickens and cows were awake in Gwinnett. Livestock pretty much got along better with each other than did human beings. Wasn't much need for police that time of night.

At shift's end officers drove their patrol cars home, and Puckett encouraged their personal use whenever and wherever. Seeing the cars out and about gave folks a sense of police presence, and in Puckett's sly mind, one less thing to worry about. The way he figured, personal use meant his boys had to keep their cars in good repair and washed clean, not so easy with all the mud and mule crap slung up from patrolling rutted dirt roads. Of course there'd be no excuse showing late for duty either. Puckett was big on early and clean.

Over the next four years, managed by Chief J. O. Bell and under the command of Assistant Chief M. J. Puckett, the Gwinnett County Police Department had in fact become the finest police force in North Georgia. We counted on them to uphold the law, and they did. In return we gave them our friendship and, more importantly, our trust.

In early spring 1964 we elected a new board of commissioners who pledged the same qualities being practiced by our police department. Things had never been better in the county, but come April 17, that would all change.

THE CRIME

Arc Road was a rutted, two-mile long, twelve-foot wide nothing of a dirt road going nowhere somewhere near the west side of the county. It was one of many dirt roads that formed rural Gwinnett, a land city folks called the country. By twelve o'clock noon on an otherwise typical beautiful day, that little dirt road would come to be known as The Point of All Evil.

Locals had eagerly awaited that morning as the kick-off to spring with weekend festivals scheduled in towns across Gwinnett. Forecasters predicted good weather would favor all three days.

A bit past eight o'clock Chief Bell answered a phone call from one of only two houses settled along the dirt road. Carl Mills told Chief Bell that his house-sitter noticed a police car parked in the woods near the top of Arc's hill. The car, backed in between small trees, looked almost hidden from the road. There was no sign of policemen, but Mills said he'd heard and seen men on the hill late the previous night.

Bell shouted across the one-room jailhouse lobby to Deputy Jerry Griswell sitting half asleep in a chair propped against the wall. "Hey Gris! Ever heard of Arc Road?"

Griswell, with one eye squinting open, said, "Huh? Arc Road? No. Where'd you say it was?"

"I didn't. Why the hell you think I'd be asking if I knew? Wake your ass up, man! Thank God it's Friday. Where is everybody?"

"Looks like just you and me, Chief."

"I don't need any of your smart-ass. Pull your car up front! Looks like just you and me is going for a little drive. Where the hell is Roberts and Sexton? Ain't they supposed to be in by now?" Bell walked toward the coffee table. "Have I gotta do every little goddamn thing around here? Shit, I ain't even had my morning coffee!"

"Where we going to on this little drive of yours?"

Bell scoffed, "What in the hell you think I been talking 'bout? Arc Road!"

"Well Chief, I ain't got no idea where this Arc road is."

Bell, slightly amused by the deputy, said, "I reckon you know what a roadmap is, don't ya?"

"Well yeah, but I don't think we got one."

Bell, nearing his last nerve, shouted, "Griswell, we are the goddamn county police. You mean to tell me we ain't got no roadmap?" Pointing across the room, he snapped at the deputy, "Turn your ass around! Tell me what the hell that is tacked up on that wall there. Well, what do you know, that's a roadmap of this whole damn county now, ain't it? You been here how long?"

"Well yeah, but we can't hardly take it down and carry…"

Bell cut Griswell off. Holding back his temper, he stared at the front door. "Where in the hell are Roberts and Sexton?" Slowly blowing out a deep breath, he slumped his shoulders. "Listen here, Griswell. Right now I'm as calm and cool as can be, and you wanna know why? 'cause I got only one more day to put up with this bullshit till I get two days away, so tell you what I'm gonna do. I'm gonna pour me a cup of coffee. I'm gonna find that damn Arc Road on this here map, and then I'm gonna walk out that door right smack into the front seat of your waiting car. You got that?"

Griswell smiled, "I got that, Chief."

Bell smirked, "Good boy."

As the chief and Griswell drove out of the front parking lot, Roberts and Sexton pulled in. Bell motioned them to follow. During their twenty-minute drive he wondered out loud to Griswell, "Why on earth would somebody just leave a cop car in the woods? If it's even a cop car." He looked at Griswell, "Of course if it is, whose is it?"

Exiting off the Northeast Expressway, Griswell drove east on Beaver Ruin Road until he spotted a simple wooden sign notched in block letters, ARC. He turned onto the dirt road that headed north up a long, gradual hill. The two Gwinnett patrol cars drove past the Mills house on their right until Bell got his first glimpse of the abandoned car. It sat a hundred yards farther, backed into the woods about fifty feet off the road's left side. The cars came to a stop near the top of the hill where they had the abandoned car in direct sight.

"Well I'll be damned, it's ours," Bell exclaimed.

"It's Twenty-nine, Chief."

Puzzled, Bell drawled, "Yeah, I can see that." He stared at the car for a short moment then told Griswell, "Call over to the jail and have somebody get hold of

Pruitt. Find out what he knows about this." Baffled, he shook his head, "What in the hell is it doing sitting out here?"

The car, a 1963 Plymouth four-door sedan, was the newest of the county fleet and assigned to officers Davis and Everett, who worked the late night to early morning shift.

The four men got out of their cars. Sexton and Roberts walked toward Twenty-nine with Bell and Griswell following a few steps behind. Tire tracks in the soft dirt showed the patrol car was first parked in the road and then driven in reverse to where it sat. The policemen looked inside the patrol car and saw that the radio microphones and roof light wires had been torn loose. In the dirt were clear impressions of a man's footprints coming out from the driver's door and leading back to the road. The prints were spaced far enough apart to indicate the person was moving quickly, probably running. The prints ended in the road at tire tracks from another car that had apparently been parked in front of the police car before it was moved. In front and just to the right side of those tracks were yet another car's tire tracks and more footprints. It was obvious that two cars and several men had gathered there in the road before continuing north over the hill.

Concerned for his officers' whereabouts, Bell radioed for assistance. Straight away he heard the whine of distant sirens coming closer. Two Georgia State Patrol cars arrived followed by one each from the cities of Duluth and Norcross. Chief Bell waved them over to the left side of the road and told the state patrolmen to skirt along the ditch and continue over the hill. The city cops stayed to help search the surrounding area.

The state patrol cars rustled up a haze of dust when they drove past. Watching them disappear over the hill

Bell felt sick to his stomach. From the woods, through the thin cloud of swirling dust, car Twenty-nine sat facing him as if teasing an eerie silent confession, "I know what happened." Bell quietly lipped, "Yeah, but you ain't talking." He looked at the tire tracks and footprints, "Something ain't right about this place."

Officer Roberts crossed the road and found a small booklet and loose papers in the ditch to the right of the lead car's tracks. A few yards farther he spotted two police blackjacks close together, one a homemade job he immediately recognized as belonging to his good friend Jerry Everett. Roberts shouted, "Hey, Chief, come look at this. It's Jerry's."

Bell stood next to Roberts looking down in the ditch. "Yeah, it's his." He paused, shook his head and then asked, "What do you figure's going on here?"

Roberts reached down to pick up the blackjacks.

Chief Bell called out, "Hold up, Jake, don't touch it. Let everything sit right where it is."

Bell called his men together. "Boys, let's everybody fan out, see if we can't find something more. I just wish I knew where those men're at."

Deputy Griswell spouted. "Chief, I got this real bad feeling they're out here somewhere, only they're dead."

"Goddamn it, Griswell! How 'bout you shut your mouth and keep a positive thought?" Bell shook his head, "My god, this place has got me to where I ain't making no sense. Things is going so fast till I had better stop and think here for a minute." He looked back at the blackjacks in the ditch and then turned around in the road to look again at the abandoned cop car in the woods. It took but a moment for the pieces to add up. "Oh Lord, we're in the middle of a crime scene. I just hope Griswell ain't right."

Topping Arc's hill the two state cars scraped their way down its opposite side. The rutted dirt road gradually fell downhill for nearly half a mile until reaching a narrow flat area shaded by the overhang of good-sized hardwoods on each side. Troopers stopped their car and stepped out. A strong smell of burnt metal and rubber broke the fragrance of fresh spring air. Through the quiet they heard the sound of running water from a stream farther down. In that direction dark smoke draped the tree branches of Arc's thick woods.

The troopers followed a bend in the road and walked not more than a hundred feet before finding a burned-out late-model Oldsmobile coupe still smoldering and wedged inside a small stand of trees. One of the troopers radioed Chief Bell with the news.

Chief Bell sent Griswell and Sexton to join the troopers while he and Roberts cordoned off the road. The two county officers slowly reached the flat bottom where they pulled behind the state patrol cars. From the left ditch grew an ancient oak tree. Its branches, entering full bloom, shaded a rundown field house. In front of the house, car tires had gouged deep tracks into the narrow road surface. Somebody had backed up and pulled forward several times in an effort to reverse direction. A disarray of numerous footprints tangled with what appeared to be drag or scuff marks that abruptly disappeared in the middle of the road. More footprints, coming and going, led to the Oldsmobile. The officers followed the prints toward the burned out car but held short from its intense heat. Obviously this was a crime scene that likely connected with the abandoned patrol car and added more suspense.

Over the radio Sexton described the scene to Bell. He told him that he and Griswell would search the area for anything suspicious.

They searched the single-room field house, then walked around the property, stepping over a sagging barbed-wire fence. They walked back out onto the dirt road and continued down toward the burned Olds. They walked past the destroyed car for another hundred or so feet until reaching the wooden bridge that crossed over Bromolow Creek. Standing on the bridge watching the creek flowing beneath, Griswell could not shake his thoughts about the lost officers. "Ray, they're here in these woods somewhere, and my gut tells me they're dead."

"Damn it, Griswell," Sexton cried out, "keep a positive mind like the chief said."

Griswell shook his head. "Nope, if they was out here and alive, we'd know it."

After searching the area for near thirty minutes, the two men walked toward their car. In front of the field shack, Sexton noticed an overgrown two-track path that at one time might have been a driveway or wagon trail. The path led beyond the house and continued up a slight grade fifty feet into the woods. He pointed in that direction. "Let's make our way up through there and give it a quick search before I call the chief."

April morning dew glazed a leaf-covered thicket hiding a patch of briar vines. Twenty feet up the path the briars snared both men by their ankles. While the men pulled themselves free, their eyes were drawn to an area of ground where the morning sun beamed a ray through the tree canopy. Each man stared tilting his head like a confused dog.

Sexton and Griswell walked forward another few steps pushing the briar vines out of their way. They shaded their foreheads to see farther into the woods, and their disbelief turned to fear. They looked at each other.

Griswell asked, "Is this real?"

They slowly walked closer before holding still. The moment would forever replay in their minds, a slow-motion cruel memory, whenever the smell of rotting leaves crumpled under their feet, the sour scent of pine tar flushed from the trees. Their fear turned to horror.

Flat on the ground, danced over by cloud shadows and scavenging insects, death presented not two but three bodies: Gwinnett County police officers Jerry Everett, Ralph Davis, and Jesse Gravitt. Everett and Gravitt lay face down, Davis on his back. Dark red blood drained into the dry soil underneath them. Davis' left arm was bent over his face, hiding his eyes and nose. His left hand and Gravitt's right hand were cuffed together, stretched across and resting along the back of Everett's right shoulder. Everett's right hand bent around the back of his neck and was cuffed to the chain of the first pair. Rigor mortis held everything in place. They had been lying in the woods all night. All three had been shot multiple times in the head.

Officer Sexton pointed at the rigid corpses, his face distorted with horror. Deputy Griswell leaned against a tree. He cupped his hand over his mouth. The two men stared. That kind of shock freezes your voice. Gradually Sexton's silence gave way to a stuttered mumble that turned into a holler, a message soon echoing through Arc's valley.

Back on the road, troopers jolted by the sound ran toward Sexton. A few minutes later the discovery began a day of broken "Say Again?" transmissions blasting through police radios all over North Georgia.

Driving his patrol car with Chief Bell in the passenger seat, Officer Roberts spun his front wheels as they topped the hill on Arc Road. Nearly fishtailing from ditch to ditch he plunged down its opposite side as the car undercarriage repeatedly slammed against the dirt road. Roberts skidded to a dust-pluming stop behind the cars, then jumped out. He ran up the path and paused fifteen feet short of Sexton and Griswell. Bell, having chased close behind, pushed him aside. He staggered a few steps forward before falling to his knees. He pounded the ground with his fists while screaming to his murdered officers, "No goddamn it! No, no, no!"

While gritting his teeth, he shook his raised head. No words followed. Bell looked at the badge pinned to his shirt pocket and screamed inside his brain, "Don't take it! I should have told the commissioner to leave my sorry ass alone so I can get on with my simple life. But no, not me! What do I do? I reach out and take it! How could I have been so damn stupid?" He had felt proud, but he didn't feel so proud anymore. "That old cop, Puckett, tried to warn me, but I wouldn't listen. Goddamn it, why didn't I listen to him?"

Like his three officers on the ground ten feet in front of him, all his high and mighty hopes of getting the county straight had died.

As Chief Bell rose to his feet he shouted at the men standing near, "Don't nobody touch nothing! Everybody stop where you're walking, backtrack to where you came, and don't nobody walk on that damn road! There's footprints here that belong to the sons of bitches who done this, I don't want nobody messing up nothing."

As he stared at his three officers on the ground Bell understood this crime was not only out of his league but out of the league of all law enforcement in Gwinnett. Nobody in the county had the know-how to investigate, let alone solve, these murders.

One of the State Patrol officers on scene alerted the Georgia Bureau of Investigation, and Director Barney Ragsdale sent Lieutenant James Stanley to Arc Road.

Ragsdale asked police chiefs in Atlanta, Fulton, and DeKalb County to assist Stanley with their best homicide detectives. In less than forty-five minutes a dozen seasoned investigators were standing at the murder scene. While staring at the bodies, several investigators emotionally reminisced of a time when they too once wore a similar blue uniform.

Alerted by the sound of wailing sirens, Gwinnett residents from miles around found their way to Arc Road. A handful strolled alongside police cars parked on the dirt road. Two men peered in the woods, and got a glimpse of the atrocity. They slowly walked to within feet of the murdered officers. Word of the crime soon carried, and in a short time a few curious locals turned into a crowd of nearly fifty and more tramping over the scene.

On the pathway, Lieutenant Stanley and detectives huddled around the bodies. As they planned their investigation, Stanley noticed his distraught officers standing in the road while the pedestrian crowd gathered behind. His calm quickly broke. Agitated, he double-stepped down the path toward his men. "What the hell are you troopers just standing there for? Get these people the hell out of here and block off this god damn road! You men do your job, or I'll find somebody who can."

With the crowd growing by the minute, Stanley realized he'd better get his investigation in gear or this thing was going to blow up in his face. His first order of business was to secure the crime scene and separate it into four areas: the abandoned police car, the road itself, the burned Oldsmobile, and finally the bodies of the murdered police officers. He divided the group of detectives into three teams and assigned each its own area to search. He sent the first team to the abandoned police car. He sent the second team back up the road to meet

Chief Bell, and the third team to the burned Oldsmobile. Stanley, and soon Dr. Larry Howard, would examine the bodies of the three policemen.

For nearly a decade the state had relied on the skills of GBI Lab Director Dr. Larry Howard, Georgia's leading medical examiner for forensic autopsy, to investigate murders. He was also an expert in ballistics and analyzing crime scene evidence. Dr. Howard received an urgent call from Stanley. He replied, "Jesus Christ, Jim, did you say three cops were murdered? Handcuffed together and murdered? Jim, you been drinking? You are joking, right?"

"Damn it, Larry, I'm up to my elbows in shit out here. Drop whatever the hell you're doing and come as quick as you can!"

From the tone of his voice Howard knew Stanley wasn't joking. "I'm on my way. Give me thirty minutes and tell your troopers to be on the lookout. And Jim, listen to me. Keep the area clear and don't let anybody in until I get there. Nobody!"

The first team of detectives dusted the patrol car for fingerprints and took inventory of its contents. In the car interior they found a straw hat next to a pack of cigarettes that sat on top of the backseat. The officer's metal logbook lay on the floor and the two microphones were ripped from the radio and thrown over the passenger seat. Wires from the roof's bubble light were torn loose, and hung down from the headliner. The car keys were nowhere to be found so a detective popped the trunk open using a crowbar. Not one single clue or shred of evidence came from either the interior or exterior or from the woods that half hid patrol car Twenty-nine.

In the middle of Arc Road, across from the car, Chief Bell sat in the front passenger seat of his patrol car with his right leg swung out the open door. He pointed detectives to the tire tracks and shoe imprints and then pointed to the ditch where they'd found the small booklet, loose papers, and two blackjacks. The small booklet was an automobile owner's manual with a name and vehicle identification number printed on the inside front cover. Detectives, while examining the burned car, heard from headquarters that a 1963 maroon Oldsmobile coupe had been reported as stolen out of DeKalb County. The name and vehicle number filed in the report were the same as those printed inside the manual. The report stated the owner, living near I-85, fifteen miles south of Arc Road, had parked the car in his apartment complex the previous night around ten thirty and discovered it missing that morning around eight o'clock.

For the second team of investigators, Arc Road's soft dirt held the clues of how the crime developed. After following the tire tracks and footprints and measuring each impression, team members came to a shared conclusion.

Detective Luke Conlin, a tall transplanted Texan wearing a Stetson hat and round-toed boots and holstering a long-barreled six-shot magnum revolver, walked up to the patrol car where Bell sat. "Chief, sir, I believe we got a good sense for what happened if now's a time you'd like to hear."

Tired and disheartened, Bell answered, "Well, ain't gonna change nothing, far as I'm concerned, but yeah, go ahead."

"Yes, sir. Well, from the way all them tire tracks are laid out, looks like Twenty-nine come from over the other side of this hill." Conlin, cool, without expression, gestured up and down the dirt road, waving his hand as he explained the findings, "These tracks along the side here more than likely are from that burnt Oldsmobile back down the other side there, the tires on that thing being so melted ain't no way of telling for sure, but probably are. Well, it come from Beaver Ruin down there. A second car come along in behind, parking right up to his bumper. No doubt they's working together. Now my guess is some sort a ruckus or another happened in this area, and here's why I say that." Pointing in the road to an area of deep tire prints, he said, "Them tracks over yonder belong to Twenty-nine. It come to a stop right in front of the Olds. Between them we got a single set of footprints that belongs to one of your officers. He got out of Twenty-nine, I reckon the driver, and probably had visuals on whoever was sitting in that Oldsmobile." Conlin leaned down to the open passenger door, making close eye contact with Chief Bell. "Course some of this is speculation on our part, but I'd say it's most likely what occurred."

Walking back out into the road, the detective continued, "Well, Twenty-nine, all of a sudden takes off, I mean in a real hurry. We know this, 'cause you got shallow tread marks turning mighty deep here. And the officer who got out of Twenty-nine, he don't get back in. He's left standing here in the road as the patrol car goes squealing off hard on the gas, the way it threw up dirt. Now back a few yards down where this second car was, same thing. He's parked behind the Oldsmobile all quiet like until he's throwing up dirt only the crazy sumbitch went backwards, hammered the damn thing in reverse. Probably got spooked whenever he seen your boys coming."

The tall Texan explained in detail, "Reason I say he was in reverse, his marks are deep and the dirt splattered from his wheels, which were his back wheels dragging the fronts side to side, the way the tracks are squirreling. Ain't no doubt he was in some kind of hurry, 'cause Twenty-nine's got him in a chase." Conlin shook his head. "Now just how dumb do you have to be thinking you're gonna outrun the police driving backwards? Pretty dang dumb, I'd say." Sharply fitted in a western style suit, the impressive Texan removed his hat and rubbed back his long, curly hair, "Might be that whoever was in that Oldsmobile done jumped out and run off, 'cause that thing didn't go nowhere. I mean it barely moved from the time it was parked until the time it went over the hill. Now this chase between Twenty-nine and the second car all came to a head in that gravel driveway down the bottom of the hill there.

"I believe what he tried doing was turn around and get out going forward, but looks like your boys caught up with him first. Wouldn't have been too awful hard. Anyway, they pulled up on him, got him blocked in some way or another, I'm sure, 'cause here they all come back again. Right here to where it started. Twenty-nine's following, but at some point pulls forward then backs up into them woods there." Conlin again leaned inside Chief Bell's car. He pointed directly at the abandoned patrol car sitting off the road in front of them. With a tone of absolute certainty he said to Bell, "And wasn't none of your boys put it up in there. No sir, wasn't no officer would've done that." The detective stood away from Bell and looked around the road. He cocked his head back and took a long breath through his nose. "Someone put that patrol car back up in there, and it damn sure wasn't for no good intentions, I'm here to tell ya."

Conlin walked a few steps in front of Chief Bell's car and then turned back around. He paused and stared up and down the dirt road. After a few moments he looked at Bell. "We figure there was three of 'em and your three officers. We're finding six different prints, six sets of shoe prints. They were walking around here in this area all bunched together. Right here is where the deal went down, and wasn't no fighting neither. No scuffs marks, no body prints. Nothing like that happened. Could of walked into a trap maybe, dropped their guard. Who knows? It sure don't make no sense, not far as I can tell." Nodding he said, "I can say this. Right here is where their jacksticks got throwed over in that ditch and right here is where they got cuffed, and the way them footprints shuffle around the lead car's tracks then disappear, that's where they got in or was put in that Oldsmobile and took over this hill. Ain't no other way your boys could've gotten down there. They damn sure didn't walk.

"We'll take photographs of all whatever, everything that's here, and make some casts of these shoe prints and tires, but my best guess is what I've been telling you is what we're gonna end up with. It's all here. Dirt don't tell no lies." Detective Conlin fixed his stare straight into the eyes of Chief Bell. "I'm sure sorry about this, Chief. I wish the world for ya when telling the families." He raised his eyebrows. "Chief, sir, don't you give it no concern, hear? We're gonna get 'em! And when we do might best look the other way. Ain't gonna be pretty."

Across and down the road from the officers' bodies the third team of detectives examined the burned Oldsmobile. The license plate was missing, but the vehicle ID in the owner's manual matched the vehicle identification number plate on the car. Other than being burned to the ground, the car was intact with no sign of missing or stripped parts. There was no need to dust the car for fingerprints; no hope in that, but later, after it was towed to the impound lot, there would be a thorough scouring for evidence. For now detectives could only wonder out loud what role the Oldsmobile played.

Standing in the cool shade and having shed his blue sport jacket, veteran Atlanta Homicide Investigator Patrick Telder led the discussion. "Okay, let's see what we got." Telder, heavyset, held a weathered Homburg in his hand. A .45 caliber 1911 pistol fit inside a brown leather shoulder holster rode under his left arm, against his chest. "All right! So we got us a police car up there sitting all quiet like and a stolen car down here burning. Between 'em we got three dead officers laid out on the ground in those woods up there." With the cold manner of an interrogator, Telder questioned DeKalb County Homicide Detective Gavin Jenkins and Fulton County Investigator Brice Gilmer, "Now why in the hell would you go through all that trouble of stealing this car in Atlanta then bring it all the way out here to the country only to set it afire?"

Detective Jenkins reasoned, "You wouldn't, unless you got something you wanted to hide."

Telder asked, "Something like what?"

"Obviously this car is the reason why those officers are dead," Jenkins said.

"It is? Well then, what might that reason be?"

Jenkins, normally cool, fumed, "Shit, reason being those officers knew the bastards who stole this car. I'll bet you anything they knew them real good; otherwise how you going to handcuff three police officers together like that?"

"I don't know. How would three police officers let someone handcuff them like that?"

Investigator Gilmer speculated, "If somebody was already holding a gun to one, the others might not have much of a choice."

"Yeah? And just how is somebody going to put a gun, say, to my head, without me noticing?"

Jenkins said, "If you knew a man well enough to trust him, turning your back for a split second is all it'd take, or if he was to come up behind you. Hell, nobody has eyes in the back of their head."

Gilmer, tired of the quibbling, said, "At this point don't none of that matter. How it started, whether they got ambushed or let their guard down or whatever, it don't make no difference. What does matter is who done it, and boys, whoever it was has murder three times riding their backs. They're gonna be runners."

Telder said, "That's not a hard secret to crack." The Atlanta investigator walked around the burned Oldsmobile and then paused to look back up the tree-lined dirt road where Stanley and the others waited for Dr. Howard's arrival. "Yeah, might be anything's possible or might be everything's possible, but this much I'm sure of. They stole this car and then brought it all the way out here for a reason, and it wasn't the same reason why it sits here burned to the ground. No, there's something that went down in this car that the killers don't want us knowing about. That's why they torched it."

Jenkins voiced his opinion, "Hell, Telder, you don't gotta be no genius to figure that out. It's all connected; this car here is the reason why they're lying dead in them woods up there. You say you wanna know what? Well I'll tell you what, and it's as simple as this. They were slaughtered by a bunch of goddamn redneck car thieves over a goddamn stolen car. That's what. And I'll tell you another thing. I'm willing to bet my pension it was locals who done this 'cause Gwinnett County ain't nothing but rednecks covered in pig vomit. Redneck shit, that's who killed 'em. Redneck shit!"

As investigators continued their work, Dr. Howard drove onto the scene and parked in front of the old shack. He walked up to the bodies. "Whoa! God almighty, they've been slaughtered. Somebody sure as hell wanted these officers dead." Beside the murdered men he knelt down on one knee to closely examine the gunshot wounds in the back of Officer Gravitt's head. "This looks more like an execution than a murder."

Lieutenant Stanley crouched along the right side of the three bodies and gently raised the brim of Officer Davis' police cap, revealing multiple gunshot wounds to his face. "Same thing here, Doc! Looks like they emptied the whole cylinder in him. Who in God's name you figure would've done something like this?"

Howard shook his head in disgust. "It wasn't done in God's name, and I'm not willing to offer up any opinion as to who or why. That's your job, but I can tell you this: you'd better catch the bastards and soon. This county's gonna be breathing down your neck every day until you do. You may not be aware, but right at this very moment there's cars parked halfway to the interstate. We'd better get a move on while we still can."

Crime scene photographer Hester Patton had arrived from his office in Lawrenceville and stood near the pathway readying his equipment.

Dr. Howard told Lieutenant Stanley, "Jim, call down to your photographer and have him come up here, please. I want closeups from every angle especially those handcuffs."

While Patton took pictures, Dr. Howard stood several feet away and stared at the handcuffed policemen on the ground. He shook his head in disappointment and mumbled, "My god, boys, how on earth did you get yourselves in this mess?"

Patton moved away to photograph the surrounding area, and Dr. Howard continued his field examination of the bodies. "Jim, you got a key to unlock these cuffs?"

"Hold on, Doc. Yeah, I got one."

Dr. Howard opened his black leather duffle bag and took out a pair of latex gloves and a magnifying glass. He first walked around the bodies, taking note of each policeman's position. One at a time he held up their hands while Stanley unlocked each cuff, trying not to disturb any fingerprints that might be found. In close examination, he found that Gravitt and Davis had small traces of dried blood smeared on their hands. Everett had a heavy blood smear on his right palm.

Dr. Howard used his magnifying glass to look at the bullet entry wounds in the head of each officer. Gunshot residue clearly indicated that the muzzle of the murder weapon or weapons was placed and fired very near or against the wound entrance. For the next few minutes he continued what was to him a familiar examination of murder at a crime scene. After kneeling and squatting alongside the bodies for almost ten minutes, he rose to his feet. With his hands pushing on each side of his lower back, he let out a groan. "Lieutenant, the way rigor has set in, I'd say they've been here for about eight, maybe ten hours. By any chance you got an ID on these boys? Who is this one on his back?"

Stanley pointed at each policeman as he called out their names, "That's Ralph Davis, this is Jerry Everett, and this one is Jesse Gravitt."

"Who did you say is this one in the middle? What did you tell me his name is?"

"That's Jerry Everett, Doc."

Dr. Howard dropped his shoulders and tilted his head forward, "I know him. Good family. Well, the way Davis' right hand is placed under Everett's armpit, it looks like he was either supporting or possibly carrying him. Mr. Gravitt might have as well, with his left hand.

I don't know why else it would be behind Everett's back like that. One might assume from their order they could have been on their knees when shot, but I don't think so. It's hard for me to believe they'd just simply kneel down to be executed, although it's obvious they've all been shot multiple times from very close range."

Dr. Howard walked around to the right side and leaned directly over Ralph Davis. Shaking his head he told Lieutenant Stanley, "With Davis here it appears they put the gun in his mouth and hammered away. Those teeth scattered over there are his." Dr. Howard continued his explanation by pointing at the other officers and their wounds. "Gravitt same thing, very close range. They put the gun against his head, the way these wounds appear. Everett has this one bullet wound in the back of his right leg and one to his right shoulder. Obviously he's got wounds in his head as do the rest, but I won't have an exact count until I examine the bodies more closely. I'm sure I'll get some fragments out of them for ballistics." He looked at Lieutenant Stanley. "Jim, do you have their guns?"

"Doc, they didn't have their guns on them when we got here. I don't know where they are."

"Well hell, they've been shot with their own guns and the killers took them. I have no doubt that's what's happened; otherwise the guns would be here. Take a look at Everett's gun belt. You see those two empty bullet slots on the back? Well, they're hard to reach. He would've pulled two that were easier to get, if needed. If you can find the guns, won't surprise me if the bullets I dig out of him match those left on his belt and ballistic tests match their guns to the bullets. Okay, let's roll them over."

Two ambulances arrived and were parking in the road. The doctor changed his plans. "I tell you what. I've seen all I need to see for now. Let's get them out of here. Tell those men to hurry up with their gurneys."

Lieutenant Stanley motioned for three folded gurneys to be brought up the path. The first one was placed on the ground next to Officer Davis. Two heavily built men, dressed in white attire, slowly picked the policeman's rigid body off the ground and placed him atop the thin gurney mattress. One man squatted down at each end and with a jerk raised the gurney while its folded chassis released underneath. The apparatus sprung into the locked position. The distinct sound caused all who were near to pause.

Lawmen standing in the road removed their hats as they turned to watch the moment. A minute later the second gurney clanked into position, and again, a third time, the metal hinges sounded. The bodies were covered and tightly tucked under white sheets. Sexton, Griswell, and several more lawmen helped the ambulance attendants maneuver each gurney down the uneven pathway out onto the dirt road. Officer Davis' left elbow, bent at an angle, jutted from under the taut sheet. Officer Everett's body was placed face down on the mattress. His right hand ghastly pointed around the back of his neck, and his legs, slightly bent at the knees, directed his feet over the left side of the gurney. Officer Gravitt was placed face down with his right arm extending awkwardly from his side. The two waiting ambulances had their rear doors open wide to receive the bodies for transport, two in one, one in the other.

Lieutenant James Stanley and Dr. Larry Howard stood in silent reverence while the gurneys were rolled down the path and placed inside the ambulances.

The dirt from where the officers died was covered in thick pools of dark red blood. Dr. Howard swept his hand around a six-foot circle, "Jim, get some of your boys to dig up this area and put it in buckets for me. No more than a couple of feet, I'd say. I want to sift through it, see if there's anything in the way of bullets or fragments. And bring me whatever you take out of that Oldsmobile, I want to see all of it. And of course the guns, if you find them. Maybe the killers tossed them out here somewhere. They wouldn't want to get caught red-handed with them."

Lieutenant Stanley answered, "Yeah, well, Doc, I'm thinking the same as you. If they're here close by, we'll find 'em."

"All right, that's fine. I'm going to head over to Sammons Funeral Home, but first I'd better get some lunch, so give me about an hour, and then you can reach me there if you need me. I'm sure I'll be there most of the night. Listen, would you do me a favor and have a couple of your troopers escort the ambulances? I'd like them front and rear, and I'd really appreciate it if they could stay at Sammons until I'm finished. I don't want to be bothered by anyone tonight."

"Sure, Doc, let me know if you need anything else."

"Okay. Thanks. I'll have you a preliminary report by Sunday, but I don't expect to find any surprises. We already know the cause of death." Dr. Howard walked down the path to his car and turned back toward Stanley. "Lieutenant, as far as I'm concerned, when you come up on those bastards, take them out then and there. Hell, I'd pull the trigger myself if you'd let me. I'll dig the lead out of their dead bodies and wear it on a chain around my neck. Make a right fine keepsake, wouldn't it?"

"You got that right. Sure would."

Lieutenant Stanley arranged for two state patrol cars to escort the ambulances during the twenty-minute ride to Sammons Funeral Home where Dr. Howard would perform the autopsies. Before the four-car convoy turned left onto paved Beaver Ruin, it raised a swirling cascade of dust over Arc Road. Their route would tie in with State Highway 29 leading to Lawrenceville.

People all along the roadside craned their necks to catch a glimpse inside the ambulances. After arriving at their destination, the patrol cars blocked off the parking lot. The two ambulances backed up against the mortuary's rear doors. All employees, including Sammons himself, were ordered from the premises. Dr. Howard would be assisted only by the undertaker.

Back on Arc Road, Lieutenant Stanley gathered the detectives in front of the crumpled field shack. "All right, you made your search. Anybody got anything? Something I need to know right now?"

The road team detectives gave a short summary about what they believed happened near the patrol car, but otherwise all the others shook their heads.

Lieutenant Stanley told them, "Here's what's going on. A car left out of here last night. Went up Beaver Ruin toward the expressway. No doubt it was the killers. They got our boys' guns. I'm almost positive they were shot with those guns, and the killers aren't gonna run with 'em. They've thrown 'em out somewhere around here and we're gonna find 'em no matter how long it takes. I ain't asking, I'm telling, I want 'em found. We'll start right here and work our way through these woods up that path. Spread out good and don't leave nothing uncovered. I don't care if you've got to scratch away every leaf on this ground. Do whatever you got to do, but find them guns. They're in here somewhere. Walk the road and these woods all the way back to the entrance. You know how to do it. Some of you..." The Lieutenant looked at the fifteen or so lawmen standing in a circle around him. He pointed to several state troopers who continued to arrive. "Now listen to me, there's a lake across Beaver Ruin in front of this road where they could've thrown the guns out when they drove off. Some of you troopers start a team, I don't care who, start a team and drag that lake until you either find those guns or you're sure they're not in there. Everybody else get started. There's gotta be casings or something, and keep those people out of here, even if you got to put 'em in jail. I don't care, just get them off this damn road. All right, you know what to look for, so get moving."

Following the Lieutenant's instructions, detectives fanned out on the road, combing through the brush and woods near the area where the bodies were found. Within a few minutes Officer Gravitt's wallet was discovered twenty-five feet from where he had fallen.

As detectives continued their search of Arc Road, state patrolmen walked across Beaver Ruin to drag the tiny reservoir named Freeman Lake. They tied horseshoe magnets to the end of long ropes and flung them out as far as they could into the shallow water. They walked along the shoreline, slowly pulling the magnets through the water, hoping to snag the guns if they were there. Several lake residents, eager to help, offered troopers the use of their johnboats to troll the lake farther out from shore. All afternoon officers pulled ropes through the cold water, but Freeman Lake gave them only rusty garbage for their efforts. As the long afternoon wore on and the tired searchers wore down, prospects of finding the guns faded. The crime scene, for the most part, had by that time been processed. Several buckets of bloody dirt, plaster molds of tire imprints from the getaway car, and six different shoeprint molds from the road were sent to

Dr. Howard's crime lab at Georgia Bureau of Investigation headquarters. The stolen Oldsmobile was hauled off to the impound yard in Buford, and county police, using a spare key, drove the abandoned patrol car out of the woods to their headquarters in Lawrenceville.

Still on the site but disappointed and frustrated, Lieutenant James Stanley called his lawmen together one last time. "Well, boys, I hate to say it, but it looks like we've been stumped. It would've been a good thing if we'd found those guns, but I believe we've done all we can do. I want your reports by this evening. Give me something, even if you've got nothing. At any rate, I know you're tired and mad, so I appreciate your efforts. I really do."

Stanley, tired himself, reeled back from his authority enough to express his frustration. "We lost three fine officers today." Never before in his tenured law enforcement career had he the need to deliver a warning brought on by the sights and senses of this horrible day. "Hell, I'm thinking it could've been any one of you. Well, all right, everybody come in close. Every blessed one of you listen up real good." Stanley watched and waited for the gathered lawmen to step close to each other and settle into a tight bunch. "We got cop killing bastards somewhere out there. They're somewhere out there right now! Y'all better know, those sons of bitches didn't give a damn about killing our boys last night and they wouldn't give a damn about whether you was lying right there with them in that morgue tonight. It could've been any one of you carried out of those woods today. Say to yourself, and you'd better believe it, 'That could've been me.' Now how do you think your family would feel if it was you? How would you feel? Think about that. Think about me having to go to your house tonight and telling your family you ain't never coming home again. God knows I wouldn't want to do that. Don't make me do that! Boys, just remember at all times, keep your attention focused to what you're doing and who you're dealing with, and you'll do fine." Stanley looked deep into the faces of the lawmen surrounding him. He stared for several somber moments.

The officers returned the stare.

Falling back into his lead character, the Lieutenant snapped, "Get your reports to me quick as you can. Now let's get the hell out of here and give these people back this damn road."

After returning to the jailhouse, Chief Bell ordered county lawmen to meet up at eight o'clock that night in the lobby of Lawrenceville City Hall. At his request they were joined by GBI Director Barney Ragsdale, agents from the Atlanta FBI office, police chiefs from every major jurisdiction surrounding Gwinnett County, and Georgia's top cop, Public Safety Director Lowell Conner. Gwinnett Solicitor Reid Merritt spoke first, explaining to officials that Gwinnett County, with its resources, was in no way capable of conducting the investigation. Merritt proposed that state law enforcement intervene on the county's behalf and, in accordance with Georgia law, he would allow the State Patrol to assume both the police murders investigation and carry out law enforcement duties in Gwinnett.

Lowell Conner then stood alongside Solicitor Merritt and addressed the group. "Reid, let me tell you, I spoke with the governor this afternoon, and he is just as upset over these murders as is everybody in this room and in this county. He instructed me to oversee this investigation. He has offered me every asset in the state's arsenal, if that's what it takes, to capture these killers and bring justice for the good people of Gwinnett. I have appointed Captain Arthur Hutchins as lead investigator and Lieutenant James Stanley as second in command. Arthur and Jim will work this case full time and report directly to me. The governor has made it clear that I am to keep him informed of all details and any developments that come from our investigation. I can assure you that we will find these killers, no matter how, no matter what, no matter where. The governor asked me to convey his deepest condolences to the officers' families. He will personally pay each of them a visit when the time is appropriate. Now please allow me just a moment."

All movement and ruffling of standing feet in the small crowded lobby came to rest.

"Chief Bell, to you and your officers, I am speaking from my heart when I tell you there are no words that accurately express the sadness I'm feeling for you, your force, and most especially the officers that brought us here tonight. I've had calls all afternoon from peace officers in every corner of this state telling me the same. If there is anything I can do, please let me know. That's all I have to say."

The cramped room, packed to its walls with hard-nosed career cops, went silent as Connor bowed his head and turned away. The sounds of sadness and anger murmured throughout the gathered cops, but nothing could match the unbridled temper of Gwinnett County Assistant Police Chief M. J. Puckett. To Puckett the murdered men were more sons than policemen. He hand-picked them, watched them grow, and spent long hours every day patrolling with them, training them, and teaching them all the angles. They were his family, his world, not just a badge pinned on a uniform. They were his whole life. With his clenched fists he slammed the desk in front of him, "Names! Give me names! Every one of you people knows somebody in this county that could've done this." With his eyes spewing fire, Puckett pointed toward the window to the sprawling parking lot outside. "Justice for my boys. Yeah there will be that. You best hope y'all find them sons of bitches before I do, Mr. Conner. You best hope so, 'cause if I do, there ain't gonna be no trial. Oh, there'll be justice, all right, but it's gonna come at the end of a damn rope." Puckett shook his index finger, "I'm gonna hang those bastards from that light pole out there. I'm gonna hang those goddamn bastards from that pole and watch 'em squirm till their eyeballs pop out. Yeah, there's gonna be justice all right. You better believe it."

Chief Bell grabbed Puckett by the arm, but Puckett's rage continued as he struggled away from his close friend's grasp. With one last outburst, Puckett made his point perfectly clear. "There's gonna be justice, I tell you all. Goddamnit there's gonna be justice."

Bell wrapped his assistant chief in a bear hug, pleading with his friend, "M. J., please, I know, buddy. I know. I'm right there with you."

Puckett finally bowed to his chief's compassionate strength. Both men stood quiet, tears covering their cheeks.

Bell maintained his powerful hug around Puckett and gently whispered, "Okay M. J., it's okay. Come on, buddy, let me take you home. Let's get out of here. I'm gonna take you home."

As Chief Bell walked a brokenhearted Puckett out of the lobby, he looked back at Connor, softly wording, "Thank you, sir, for coming out."

The top cop replied, "Yes sir, Chief. Don't you worry. I promise we're gonna get 'em. On that you have my word."

The men quietly filed out of the building, got in their cars, and left, but Director Conner and Lieutenant James Stanley stood together alone in the empty parking lot.

Without asking, Conner gave Stanley a cigarette while he gazed at the light pole, "You know something, Jim? I believe Puckett means what he says. I think he'd really do it."

Stanley flicked his lit cigarette toward the pole. "Oh shit, Conner, what the hell are you talking about? Let me tell you something, I know for a fact he'd do it, and I'd be damned if I didn't help him tie the rope. Bet your sweet ass I would. Shit, it's been a long day. Too damn long! I'm going home and drink me half a bottle of liquor. See if that sets me in a better mind. I'll see you."

THE AUTOPSIES

Inside Sammons Funeral Home the harsh lights burned late into the night for Dr. Larry Howard. Earlier that afternoon he'd arrived to find the officers' bodies aligned side by side on three narrow stainless-steel tables. During his decade-long tenure as Georgia's forensic coroner, he performed many autopsies in the funeral home's backroom morgue. Always one for cleanliness, Howard took a quick look over the familiar surroundings. The cinderblock walls and concrete floor were covered in thick gloss-white paint. The waterproof floor tapered to a centered twelve-inch drain. A tarnished fine mesh screen covered its opening. Bright ceiling lights reflected off all the surfaces, casting no shadows. The wall-mounted thermostat was set to cold. If not for the officers' blood-covered blue uniforms, the white room with its stainless-steel cutting tools would have almost no color at all.

In the doorway Dr. Howard stared at the bodies.

He shook his head and wondered out loud, "Boys, what in the world could you have done that would make someone do this to you? There was no call for this. I mean one bullet is enough, but good Lord, they sure had no intention of leaving any doubt. I hope it wasn't as simple as you just wearing that badge. I've got a lot of friends that wear badges. I'd hate to think it's just that." He looked closely at the bodies for evidence. "Well, boys, why you'd want to be a police officer is totally beyond me. You'll get little if any respect, I'll say that. You'll work long hours for lousy pay. Believe me, I know. Won't have a family life, because you won't be home, you'll be out all day and night patrolling the roads. Barely have enough change in your pockets for a sandwich, let alone a decent meal, and boys, the very people you're out there protecting will be trying to stab you in your back the moment you turn around. You'd go through all that, and for what? So you can end up here on these tables with your brains blown out? Give me one good reason why you would want to be a cop." The doctor shook his head. "That was your choice, and I'm sure for good reasons, but if you could do it all over again, knowing then what you know now, would you?"

Standing back from the tables and looking at the bodies he continued, "I'm not asking you, Officer Everett. I know you would, but Mr. Gravitt, Mr. Davis, I don't know the two of you, so I can't say for sure. But Jerry, Lord have mercy, you're just like the rest of your family—stubborn. Can't tell you nothing you don't want to hear. Boys, forgive my callous mood, it's just that I'm angry. I have the utmost respect for your profession; it is an honorable one, and I admire you for it. I only hope those folks over on that dirt road feel the same, but somehow I doubt it."

Dr. Howard assigned a case number to each officer's body. Speaking with a loud voice into a tape recorder by his side he began his examination of the bodies.

"Subject: Everett, Jerry R. Employer: Gwinnett County. Occupation: police officer. Place: Sammons Funeral Home. Time: two o'clock PM Date: April seventeen, nineteen sixty-four. Time and date of death: approximately two o'clock AM, April seventeen, nineteen sixty-four. Place of death: Guthrie Farm, Arc Road, Gwinnett County. Body removed from scene.

"External Examination: The body is that of a well-nourished, well-developed, young, white male, fully clothed in police uniform attire, first seen lying on his face, handcuffed to officers Davis and Gravitt. Hair is black, receding hairline, eyes are brown, pupils dilated. Multiple blood stains around face and head with anterior drainage. Fresh blood in both auditory canals, considerable blood in mouth also. Hematoma at right upper eyelid. Fresh horizontal abrasion on left side of forehead above left orbital ridge. Horizontal blood stain of right palm and surface of middle finger. Examination of fingernails is not remarkable. Bullet wound of entry in pants back of the right leg approximately fifteen inches below waist in middle of crease. Apparent wound of exit just to the right bottom of zipper. Blood drainage from exit wound is front towards knee. Rigor is present."

Howard leaned over Officer Gravitt. "Subject: Gravitt, Marvin, J. Employer: Gwinnett County. Occupation: police officer. See Everett for details.

"External Examination: the body is that of a middle-aged, white male, fully clothed in police uniform attire. The body was first seen lying on his face handcuffed by his right hand to the left hand of Officer Davis. A second pair of handcuffs connected the right hand of Officer Everett to the first set of handcuffs. The hair is reddish gray. The eyes are gray with pupillary dilation. Blood exuding from the nose. Rigor is present."

He leaned over Officer Davis. "Subject: Davis, Ralph, K. Employer: Gwinnett County. Occupation: police officer. See Everett for details.

"External Examination: The body is that of a middle-aged white male, well developed, well nourished, fully clothed in police uniform attire. The body was first seen on its back handcuffed by his left hand to the right hand of Officer Gravitt. A second pair of handcuffs connected the right hand of Officer Everett to the first set of handcuffs. Hair short, black streaked with gray, eyes brown, pupils and cornea not remarkable. Multiple blood stains draining posteriorly from the mouth and nose. Two light horizontal scratches below left ankle. Rigor is present."

He asked the funeral home undertaker to join him in the morgue for assistance. "Please help me remove their uniforms. I need to inventory their personal effects. I'll call out the items, and if you would, please write them down on this pad as I describe them. Let me know if I'm going too fast for you and I'll slow down.

"Jerry Everett: general description, clothing and personal effects: Gun belt containing twelve metal-piercing .38 special HP bullets, five lead HP .38 special bullets, empty holster, brown leather belt with initial E on silver buckle. One blue officer's coat, bloodstained, badge over left pocket, nameplate over right pocket. One light blue officer's shirt bloodstained around the neck with bullet hole in right sleeve. One pair blue officer's pants, bloodstained with through bullet hole in right leg. One pair white jockey shorts, white cotton undershirt, one pair black oxfords, and one pair white cotton socks. One each: jack knife, key with City Recappers ring, Vicks inhaler. One set brass knuckles, four matchbooks, package of Rolaids, four sticks Beechnut gum, toothpicks, gold signet ring, four Winston cigarettes. Brown leather wallet, no folding money, two dollars thirteen cents change, Gwinnett County Police badge, business cards. Black tie with revolver clasp, automatic pencil, Ruxton wristwatch. Front right pants pocket containing small .22 caliber derringer, unloaded with two loose .22 long rifle bullets.

"Gravitt, Marvin J. (Jesse): general description, clothing and personal effects: gun belt and empty holster, cartridge holder containing six copper clad .38 special bullets, empty blackjack sheath. One pair blue shorts, one pair white cotton socks, white undershirt, one pair officer's pants, one light blue cotton shirt, bloodstained collar and back. One blue officer's coat bloodstained around the neck, with M. J. Gravitt nameplate over right pocket, with whistle, badge over left pocket. One bloodstained officer's cap, size seven and a quarter, with bullet perforations and silver band loosened by bullet passage. One pair black motorcycle boots. White linen handkerchief, black tie with Mason clip, gold pen and pencil set. One pair glasses, two cigars, box of matches, twenty-five cents (quarter), pipe with one package half & half, and one yellow comb. Three pocket knives, one Camillus, owned; two Craftsman brand not belonging to victim.

"Davis, Ralph K.: general description, clothing and personal effects: gun belt and empty holster; one officer's cap, size seven; pair of black oxfords; brown leather belt with gold buckle; blackjack sheath. One blue officer's shirt, bloodstained, white undershirt, bloodstained. One blue officer's coat, bloodstained collar and shoulders with badge over left front pocket, whistle on right front pocket. One brown wallet with Gwinnett County Police badge, no folding money, seventy-two cents in change, and key. One pair officer's pants, black socks, white handkerchief, white pencil, silver and gray pen, black tie with revolver clasp. One Elgin gold wristwatch, two white tablets with E trademark, half book matches, and four Salem cigarettes."

After completing the inventory, Howard sealed their belongings in white plastic bags. Each bag was labeled in black ink with the officer's name, case number, and date, April 17, 1964. Looking at the list he was once again reminded of the stark existence of a police officer. Compounding the bleakness, three of the trade's finest lay before him, with jagged facial wounds and staring through glazed eyes.

Their uniforms removed, Dr. Howard continued his external examination, speaking into the microphone of the tape recorder. While describing and measuring the carnage he took several infrared pictures to note bullet-powder tattooing. This phase would end as all others; stretching his lower back and drinking another cup of coffee. He said to the undertaker, "I'm going to do the internal exams now, but I have only this one filter mask, so you'll need to leave the room. It will take me until... well, it should be around ten or eleven o'clock before I'm done. Do you think you could either stay or come back about that time to tidy up?" When the undertaker agreed, the doctor continued, "I sure appreciate it. Put your inventory list on the desk out there for me, please, and let the officers outside know how long I'll be. Thank you." Dr. Howard wrapped himself in a full white gown, pulled on shoe covers, and snapped his hands into two pairs of rubber surgical gloves. He fit the mask over his nose and mouth and then placed a clear shield over his face.

First to be examined was Jerry Everett. His wounds would require an internal examination of both chest cavity and skull. The exams of officers Gravitt and Davis would track bullet wounds to the skull only. It was a thorough dissecting probe quite necessary for the record's official cause of death.

After completing the autopsies, Dr. Howard filled out a death certificate for each officer. Coming as no surprise he ruled that the three officers were all victims of homicide. In medical terminology, the cause of death read "Exsanguination and cerebral trauma secondary to multiple bullet wounds of face and head." Officer Gravitt had been shot five times; once in the face, twice in the right side of head, and twice in the back of head. Of the five shots, four would have caused instant death. Officer Davis had been shot five times in the face, any one of which would have resulted in instant death. Officer Everett had been shot six times; once in the back of the right leg, once in the right shoulder, once through the mouth, once in the right side of head, and two in the back of the head. Of the six bullet wounds, four would have been instantly fatal.

The doctor filled out the required documents releasing the bodies to funeral homes chosen by the families.

For the medical examiner the grisly work of three consecutive homicide autopsies was over. Monday morning he would resume his part of the investigation, examining crime scene evidence in his lab at GBI headquarters. For Dr. Howard it had been a long, grueling day. Totally exhausted both mentally and physically, he left the morgue shortly before midnight.

To some, Dr. Howard was a cold, heartless medical examiner, and at first appearance it might have seemed true, but given all the horror he saw in his career, that label was unfair. A medical examiner must always keep personal feelings separate from work, a discipline vital to sustain longevity while maintaining sanity. For grieving families who knew him he was a gentle man with a warm heart.

Walking out of the room through the same door he'd entered nine hours earlier, feeling equal parts anger, disgust, and sorrow, Dr. Howard glanced back one last time at the cold stainless-steel tables bearing the three corpses. "Dear God, please bless these boys and their families, and thank you for not making me a police officer."

THE FUNERALS

April 17, 1964, the clock hands spun quietly past midnight, officially marking the end of day. It was a milestone unnoticed by three grieving families. The day had begun with high hopes for the weekend's spring festival, a Native American tradition celebrating the land wakening from winter. It ended with residents' disbelief and would forever be known as the darkest day in Gwinnett history. Instead of making plans to attend festivities, folks throughout the county were making plans to attend funerals. Shortly after midnight, state troopers carried the three officers, sealed in body bags, out the rear door of the morgue. Each body left in an ambulance escorted by police to their family's chosen funeral home. Officers Davis and Everett were both taken to Tapp Funeral Home in Buford.

Davis' brother Clyde and two of Everett's brothers, George and Kelly, stood in the parking lot waiting for the ambulances to arrive. Undertaker Ryman Pendley, one of the most respected funeral directors in the county and a country gentleman waited inside. To the Davis and Everett families, Ryman was a close friend and had known the two officers since their childhood. Planning for a long night ahead, Pendley readied two caskets he had pulled from his storage building. The ambulances drove into the lot and parked inside the funeral home's arched breezeway. Troopers brought the bodies through an open door to the preparation room. Following routine protocol, Pendley unzipped the body bags only enough to see the faces, verifying their identity for the mortuary register.

First he opened Jerry's. "Good Lord," he voiced an unintentional reaction. "They told me it was bad, but I never figured on it being this bad." Pendley stood back and shook his head.

He unzipped the bag containing the body of Officer Davis. "Oh Jesus, Ralph." He stepped back again, glancing back and forth at the officers' heads protruding from the small openings in each bag. "Just look at what they done to you boys." Their faces, shattered by gunfire, were so badly bruised that they were almost unrecognizable. Almost, even for someone who knew them since birth. Pendley made a quick assessment of how he was going to hide Dr. Howard's work and repair those "nasty" bullet wounds. Next came the hardest part of his job. He somehow had to persuade the boys outside to leave. They had been waiting hours to see their brothers, but he was not about to let that happen, not looking the way they did.

Pendley called them into the parlor. "Boys, there's no need in y'all staying up here tonight, there ain't nothing here for you to do. Why don't y'all go on home and be with your families?"

George, predictably brash, replied, "Nope, me and Kelly want to see our brother now."

Clyde spoke up. "Mr. Pendley I ain't waited all this time for nothing, and I don't feel like waiting no longer. Let me see Ralph!"

"No, Clyde, you'll be able to see him in the morning when I get finished." Pendley was being as stern as he dared, "Boys, I'm asking you real nice, but I mean it. Best y'all go on home and leave me be. George, you and Kelly ought to be with your mama and daddy. Y'all come back in the morning when everything's ready."

George, mule stubborn like all the Everetts, raised his voice. "You listen here, Mr. Pendley, we're gonna see Jerry, and that's all there is to it."

"No, George, you listen to me. I ain't gonna argue with you, there ain't gonna be no arguing in this home. Jerry wouldn't stand for it, and I ain't neither. Boys, I know how y'all feel, but there ain't no need to worry. I'm gonna take real good care of 'em, so let me do what I know is best." Pendley stretched his arms wide to usher the brothers from the parlor. "Come on, let me walk you outside."

Giving in to the wise undertaker, the victims' brothers bowed their heads and relented.

Before Clyde left, he said, "I've got Ralph's suit out in the car. If you'd like, I'll go get it."

"Yes, that'll be fine, Clyde, I'll walk with you."

"It's maybe a little wrinkled, the way he kept it and all."

Smiling, Pendley promised, "I'll make sure it looks nice. We'll get it looking mighty nice for him. Oh, and George, Ray Sexton already brought me a brand-new uniform for Jerry. Mighty sharp. Got his badge and name tag too. I'm sure that's what he'd want."

"Thank you, Mr. Pendley, I'm sure he would."

"I know he would," said Kelly.

Pendley exclaimed his farewell from the heart. "Boys, I'm sorry. Real sorry. That's all I know to say. I'll have your family in my prayers. Tell 'em for me, will ya?"

❧

Twelve miles south of Buford, Jesse Gravitt's son, Marvin, sat alone on the porch at Patterson Funeral Home in Duluth. The early morning quiet was broken only by the drone of tires from an occasional truck passing on Highway 23. Draped over his arms tight in his hands was his dad's best suit of clothes, called for by the undertaker. The recently worn suit still held a faint whiff of his dad's last cigar. The familiar smell reminded him of many cool nights when the two of them sat on their front porch making plans for the future. As his gaze fixed on the funeral home sign he realized the dreams he and his father had shared were suddenly gone.

❧

Chief Bell, too wired to sleep, made use of the night, mapping out routes for police to escort the funeral motorcades. Leaving his house shortly before sunrise, he took the instructions to the funeral homes for use later that afternoon. When he walked up the front steps of the Patterson Funeral Home he saw Marvin, sitting alone, on the porch. "Son, you been up here all night?"

"Yes, sir." Marvin replied.

"I spect you ain't had no sleep either, have you?"

"That's all right, Mr. Bell."

"Marvin, I don't know how to say I'm sorry. I just don't. Your daddy meant the world to me, to all of us.

We're gonna miss him. Ain't gonna be the same. Ain't nothing gonna be the same."

"Yes, sir."

"Last week we were talking about that baby of yours and Josie's. You know, he was real proud of you two. And, oh, how he loved that granddaughter of his, more than anything. He's told me that she was his world. All y'all were. Yep, he was real proud. Son, your daddy was as fine a man as ever, and a damn fine officer. The whole county thought as much. How's your mother holding up?"

"Well, Chief, you ought a be able to figure that out for yourself."

"Yeah, son, I can. I sure can. Marvin, we're all gonna miss him something awful. I don't know if your dad told you but I'm leaving the department. I've got to turn it loose, getting too far on to keep up anymore. Told him last week. Told the commissioner too. Jess would've made one fine commissioner. He would've been just right for this county. Least that's what I thought. Told him that too. Could've done a lot of good for the folks around here. Let me take them clothes inside, I figure they're gonna need 'em soon."

"Thank you, Chief, but I reckon I'll hold on to 'em till they ask. You know, Dad cared for all y'all too. He loved his job. Was proud to be with the County. Real proud."

"Marvin, how about letting me take you home? We'll stop and get us a cup of coffee, maybe some breakfast. What do you say we do that?"

"No, Chief, I think I'll just stay right here, but thank you anyway."

"You sure?"

"Yeah, Chief, you go on. I'll be fine. Thanks."

"Well, okay. We'll be bringing your dad home this afternoon. I'll see you then, if you're sure you don't need anything right now."

"No, sir, thank you. Guess I'll see you at the house later."

"Okay, son, later."

Concerned about his officers' appearance, Bell went inside to check the progress made by the funeral home. In the preparation room, he looked at his friend, Jesse Gravitt. With a nod of approval, Bell told the undertaker, "He looks good. Y'all done a fine job. He was a good man. Jess here was a Mason, you make sure to put his pin on. Y'all look here. I want everything to go real smooth. You make sure that hearse of yours is all spiffed up real nice like. We're gonna have a big motorcade out here for Mr. Gravitt. They ain't ready just yet, probably be in a few hours or so, but I'll let you know when we're moving out. Just remember, everything's gotta go real smooth. You got that? I'm heading up to Buford. If you need me for anything, or think I need to know anything, call the sheriff's office. They can get hold of me on my radio. Y'all done a fine job. I thank you for that."

The previous twenty-four hours had been the worst day of Chief Bell's life. With no sleep, running on who knows how many cups of black coffee, his mood turned cranky.

The drive to Tapp Funeral Home alone with his thoughts made matters worse. "How are the families doing? Where are those sons of bitches who murdered my officers?" By the time he pulled into Tapp's parking lot, his nerves were frayed. From the parlor an agitated Bell shouted out, "Ryman, you in here?"

Pendley, tired, frustrated himself, shouted back, "Hello. Yes, I'll be right out." He walked into the parlor. "J. O., I wasn't expecting you here. Good morning."

"Hell, Ryman, there ain't nothing good about it. You got 'em ready yet?"

"Well yeah. Come on back, and I'll show you. Now, J. O., I done the best I could, considering."

"Considering what?"

"You know what, the way they was, the way I got 'em. Here take a look." Pendley opened Everett's casket.

Bell coughed, swallowed hard, and shouted, "Oh goddamn, Ryman! That don't even look like Jerry! Good lord! You gotta be kidding me! This won't do. No way in hell will this do." Bell took a deep breath and then slowly blew it out of his nose. "All right, let me take a look at Ralph. Open this damn thing up. Let me see what he looks like."

Pendley opened the lid of Officer Davis' casket.

"Jesus Christ, Ryman!" Bell grabbed the casket rim, rolled his eyes, and shook his head. "My god, Pendley! You don't expect me to take him home like this. Hell, I can't let them families see their boys looking like this. Not either one. Is this the best you can do?" Bell continued his emotion-filled tirade. "Would you look at what that goddamn Dr. Howard done? That looks like hell the way he put them back together. Like tore out patches on a rag-doll."

"J. O., you need to settle down before you blow a gasket. Dr. Howard did the best he could. You know that."

"Doctor my ass, he's a goddamn butcher is what he is! Look at their faces, Ryman! Ain't there nothing you can do? I'm not gonna let them people see their boys looking like this! Ain't no way in hell I'm gonna do that."

"Well, J. O. I could put a sheet of glass over Ralph. Still be able to see him, but at least they won't be able to touch him. That'd be what's best anyway, with him being so fragile and all."

"Well then, Ryman, do it. What about Jerry here? Look at his face. Can't you do something to his face?"

"I can't fix something that ain't there. You can't expect me to do miracles."

"Well can't you at least pull his skin back on that cheek?"

"Like I said, I can't fix what ain't there. I can do the same as Ralph, put glass on top of him."

"No, hell, his daddy ain't gonna sit still for that. Pendley, I gotta tell you this ain't good. You gotta do something I don't care what, you got to do something!"

"Well, maybe you want to give me some idea as to what, because look, we can go round and round on this thing, but that ain't gonna solve nothing. What you see is what you're gonna get."

"Well, oh Lord, I hate to think how Jerry's family is gonna take this. God help me. God help us all when they see him like this. And oh hell, then there's Puckett. He ain't seen 'em yet either. Boy, he's gonna have a royal shit fit whenever he does, I can guar-an-tee that. All right, listen. Take Ralph home first, whenever you get that glass. I'm gonna go out and see the Everetts, see if I can somehow explain this thing." Chief Bell looked straight down at the floor and shook his head. "Maybe try to convince them to keep this damn lid closed. Okay, I'm gonna have police cars out here soon. They'll escort you to Ralph's. Tell 'em how to get out there, will ya? I tell ya the truth, this is sure gonna be some kind of shit day! Listen. I didn't mean to…"

Pendley interrupted the irritated chief. "That's fine, you don't need to say nothing else, I understand how you feel. You just need to get some rest, that's all. I wish I could make it all better, I truly do. But that's not for us to question. Best thing for you, 'cause you're right, it's gonna be some kinda day. Best thing for you is get some rest. Look, before I forget, I've got something for you." Pendley retrieved a small plastic bag from the preparation table. Sealed inside was a bloody piece of lead. "Here, I dug this out the back of Jerry's neck. It's a bullet. I felt it when I was moving him. Give it to Doc Howard. He's gonna want it. Tell him I found it just under the skin in the middle of Jerry's neck. I probed the path; it was shot through his mouth, shattered the stem and ended up just under the skin. He wouldn't of found it unless he felt it like I did. Probably don't make no difference, but here it is anyway."

"Sure thing, I'll see that Doc gets it. Look, Ryman, I am truly, well hell, I know you done the best what you could, and I'm truly…"

"Go on, get outta here. Let me finish up my work and uh, forget about this. Hey, but look here, I think it best you maybe ease off the coffee a little, okay?"

"Yeah, maybe you're right. Call me if you need me. Call the sheriff's office. They'll get me. Be seeing ya."

By mid-morning both funeral homes had finished preparing the officers' bodies. In their caskets, they were carted to and locked down inside the carriage bay of their separate hearses. Generally, as folks do in the country, the boys would be brought home for an all-night open-casket wake. As the morning progressed, city, county and state patrol cars from all over Georgia and as far away as Alabama, the Carolinas, Florida, and Tennessee came to Gwinnett. The streets of Buford, Duluth, Sugar Hill, and Suwanee were covered in police cars. They lined the motorcade routes, parking on both sides of the road.

Saturday afternoon two hearses, loaded, rolled out. One carried the body of Officer Jesse Gravitt from Patterson Funeral Home. One carried the body of Officer

Ralph Davis from Tapp Funeral Home. Before and after each hearse, patrol cars escorted them with beacons flashing. Police cars parked along the roadside all had their emergency lights and roof top bubbles activated while the uniformed lawmen stood at attention as the procession drove by.

ℰℐ

This time the day before, just after the bodies were discovered, radio and television stations in Atlanta interrupted their regular programs to report preliminary news that three Gwinnett County police officers had been shot. The sketchy information quickly developed into reports of a horrific triple murder on a desolate dirt road. Between initial reports and final details, families of the three policemen had no idea that those officers were theirs. Going about their usual business, some tending to chores while the others went off to school or work, none were aware of the breaking news.

Officer Jesse Gravitt had worked hard and sacrificed all his life. Since childhood he farmed and raised livestock with his dad. In his late teens he took a full-time job as a machine operator at the Gin Murray Mill in Atlanta. On summer weekends he built houses with a construction crew, and in the fall he pulled the night shift at a slaughterhouse. After his Army days, he worked as a layout draftsman with the Jervis Webb Conveyor Company for fifteen years before joining the county police department. He'd built a four-bedroom house for his wife and mother in Duluth where he enjoyed, after years of clock punching, a comfortable country existence.

A veteran cop, only one month shy of his fifty-third birthday, Officer Gravitt had created a routine life and schedule. He and his partner Leonard Bowen's patrol shift ended at three AM. After filling out the duty log, Bowen would drive Gravitt home in their patrol car. He'd change his uniform for night clothes and head out to his chaise lounge on the front porch. With a Tampa Nugget in one hand and a shot glass of Canadian Club in the other, he'd sit reading his newspaper until he went to sleep in the spare bedroom so not to disturb Geneva in her last few hours of sleep.

At noon April 17, Jesse's mother, Mary Gravitt, known as Mamie, was sitting on their front porch reading her Bible. Ed Byers, a close family friend, drove straight to the Gravitt house after hearing news about the shooting on his two-way radio. Byers had a gut feeling it might be Jesse. When Byers asked if Jesse was awake, Mrs. Gravitt told him to look in the spare bedroom and see. He walked across the living room and quietly opened the bedroom door. Jesse's bed, properly made, was empty. Dropping his shoulders, he lowered his head and whispered, "Dear God, it's Jess."

He eased the door shut, walked out on the porch, and without saying a word about the empty room, calmly told Mamie, "I'll come back later."

From the look on his face she sensed something was wrong. She walked to the bedroom and cracked the door barely open, seeing for herself Jesse wasn't there. At first she thought maybe he left the house earlier while she took her mid-morning nap, but it wouldn't be like him to leave without breakfast. From the open porch door she saw an Atlanta Police car pull in the driveway. In her heart she was certain there was trouble. That car wouldn't have come all this way for no good reason. Mamie Gravitt sat down on her living room sofa and cried.

❧

Officer Ralph Davis was a humble, quiet man, mild but not meek. He came from a simple background and lived in a simple world. Telling folks he was born wearing overalls, Ralph Davis grew up in a planting field and truck farmed from the moment he could reach the steering wheel. Four years before, he had traded his overalls for a blue police uniform. Now he was ready to trade it back.

The happiest days of Officer Ralph Davis' life were behind and in front of him, when he'd farmed and, he hoped, where he would soon return. As he patrolled the dirt roads of the county's rich farmland, the smell of freshly plowed red Georgia clay mixed with manure fertilizer filled the air. The sweet smell of his happy past nagged at him as a reminder that another planting season had just passed him by. Lately, he and his wife, Gertrude, talked more and more of starting a farm when the time came for him to retire from police work. Six weeks into his forty-eighth year, he promised her it would be his last one wearing a badge.

On normal days Officer Davis' patrol shift ended at five AM. After filling out the duty log, his partner, Jerry Everett, would drive him home to Sugar Hill. Gertrude would fix breakfast and they would chat for an hour before she went to work. On the morning of April 17, Gertrude Davis sat alone in the living room of their plain two-bedroom house when her brother-in-law, Clyde, came in the front door.

He'd heard about the shooting on his radio and feared it might be his older brother. He asked her, "Has Ralph come home from work yet?"

"No, and I haven't heard from him either. He must be running late." She was concerned. He always called to let her know. From the empty stare in Clyde's eyes, she knew something was wrong. Through the living room window she could see two Gwinnett County sheriff cars pulling into the driveway. She knew those cars weren't there for a social visit and Clyde would not leave his store and come out here this time of morning just to check on Ralph. Gertrude Davis stared at her husband's empty chair. She was afraid, and she began to cry.

დ

Police Officer Jerry Everett asked for only one thing in this world, to be a cop. And he was, every bit a cop. Folks who knew him said the good Lord broke the mold after making Jerry. The finest police officer to have ever patrolled Gwinnett County, he began his police career at the age of twenty-two. Six years later he was a veteran cop skilled in every facet of the job. Two years earlier, at twenty-six, he was appointed Assistant Chief, but office work and paper shuffling wasn't meant for Officer Everett. His place was driving the roads in a police car. With a genuine will to serve and protect and his rugged boyish good looks, Jerry Everett was without a doubt the most popular cop in the county.

Officers Everett and Davis patrolled the county's west side from eight PM until five AM

They had partnered for three years and were the best of friends. At all times they had each other's back. They could anticipate each other's moves and communicate without saying a word. In most cases they got out of any jam they got in, but in all cases, they never gave up, no matter what it took. Although they shared driving duties, unless Davis needed the patrol car, Everett kept it during the day. At the end of their shift, Jerry drove Ralph home and then made the ten-minute trip to his parents' house in Suwanee. Before sunrise he'd take his German Shepherd, Thor, for a thirty-minute run through the pine country woods. Fifteen Everetts lived in three houses, all next to each other. Officer Everett would, depending on who was where, grab the first available bed, either at his parents' house, in his brother's bedroom, or across the street in a duplex with his wife, Joyce, and their three children. For the Everetts, it was a "make do with what you got" way of life.

On the morning of April 17, like most mornings, Carrie Everett, family matriarch, wore a long apron and had a dozen grandkids swarming around her feet. She took care of them during the day while their parents were working. Carrie gave no thought to Jerry's whereabouts that morning. She didn't worry if his police car wasn't parked outside or if he wasn't sleeping in her two younger boys' bedroom.

While she fixed the kids lunch, her attention was taken by the sudden appearance of a black sedan parking in the front yard. She watched as three men wearing dark suits got out of the car. The men had a serious business look about them. Strapped to each man's waist belt hung a holstered revolver sided by a gold badge. Four of her boys were policemen; right away she knew the accessories identified the men as being detectives.

Removing her apron and wiping her hands, Carrie told the children, "I want all y'all to hurry now, go play out in the backyard and stay there till I call for you. Now get!"

She walked out on the front porch, but before she could ask the men "Can I help you," a car racing toward the house at high speed came over the hill kicking up a cloud of dust from the dirt road. The car, engine blown, exhaust blowing out a plume of smoke, skid to a stop between her and the detectives. It was her husband, Lee, his face filled with panic as he leaped from the driver door. With her heart pounding from the frantic commotion and with an intuitive fear, she cried out to Lee, "Dear God in heaven! Daddy, please tell me what's going on."

He ran to her and wrapped his arms around her shoulders and held her tight. Heavy tears rolled down his cheeks. His voice choked. "Mama, it's Jerry, he's gone, Mama he's gone."

For the next hour, bosses, coworkers, and friends secretly planned strategies to send the family members home. They were torn between breaking the news and being remembered as the one who had done so.

Friday evening the three families each gathered in their separate homes, all in disbelief. Most members hoped that if they could sleep, they would wake up in the morning to find they'd only had a dark nightmare, experienced at one time or another by all police families that seldom, thankfully, comes true.

But Saturday afternoon, as the funeral motorcade arrived, family members' disbelief became a cruel reality.

Troopers had cordoned off the street for a clear parking area. Clyde Davis stood on his late brother's front porch as the motorcade arrived. Sugar Hill residents with sympathy baskets of flowers and food hanging on their arms settled across the street to watch the heart-wrenching ceremony.

Gathered at the rear hatch of Tapp Funeral Home's black hearse, six police officers wearing full dress midnight-blue uniforms stood at attention. Strict protocol directed their apparel, their appearance, their every move in performing honor guard duty. Each wore white gloves half hidden beneath jacket sleeves laced with a gold braid.

Leather belts, boots, and hat brims were all black-buffed to a high gloss. Chrome hat badges, coat buttons, and metal buckles were all polished to a bright luster. Black silk ribbons wrapped their police shields, shining strong but broken above their breast pockets.

Two rows of three officers faced each other as they slid the casket out of the coach bay. Slowly, in rigid cadence, they marched away from the hearse to the porch. Stopping at the front door, the rhythmic "thump-clap" of footsteps continued six more times. Carefully maneuvering through the narrow entrance, they carried the casket into the living room, and placed it atop a metal bier veiled in black curtains.

A day and a half earlier, Officer Davis drove off for another normal police-duty shift. One day later, he had finally come home. The honor guard, cleared from the house, took their places "at attention" on the front porch. Solemn florists, discreetly poised near the backyard, quietly moved in behind the officers to arrange floral displays sent from all over the county. The honored sacred-duty casket spray of white roses surrounding a single red rose signified that therein lay a police officer killed in the line of duty.

Running the back wall's length, eight large easels of white chrysanthemums calmed the harsh eastern sunlight radiating into the room through two picture windows. Vases of white and red roses filled every alcove. To the left of the bier stood a wreath of mixed roses. A banner stretching across read Georgia Police Chief Association. To the right stood the same roses as on the left. Its banner read Gwinnett County Police Department. The flowers' sweet fragrances belied the somber room's content.

Ralph's mother, Avery, and his four sisters sat with his wife Gertrude in the back bedroom. They were huddled together in quiet prayer. Clyde, alone, walked up to the front of the mahogany casket. He opened the top. Jolted by the sight of his brother's corpse, he dropped, face down, and sprawled his open hands across the glass lid. He heaved in a swell of emotion, crying heavily. His mind raced through a lifetime with his brother growing up together: the sudden loss of their dad years before, the back-breaking field work they shared to pay off the family bills and, of course, the good times, all the fun they'd had the way brothers do. Those were the hardest memories, the ones that recalled the good times. He felt alone without his older brother, the one who knew him best, the only person he could always rely on. He turned off the lamps and drew the curtains so the light in the room would reflect off and not through the tinted glass covering his brother's fate.

Palms down, he again placed his hands on the glass and whispered, "Ralph, I'll go get Mama."

Spirit broken, Clyde found his mother in the back bedroom sobbing in an awful swaying motion. Without her noticing, he looked at the sisters, shaking his head several times. The silent gesture told them it was bad.

Holding his mother's hands gently, he said, "Mama, Ralph's here. How 'bout we go be with him? I'll be with you. We'll all be here with you. We'll all see him together, okay? Please don't cry," Clyde pleaded. "Ralph's with Daddy now. Can't you just see him now, how happy he is, being with Daddy? And don't you know Daddy's happy? They's just a hooting and a hollering! And with Jesus they are, so Mama, please don't cry."

Clyde took his mother by the arm and walked her into the living room.

Accustomed to seeing her husband's overstuffed chair, Gertrude broke into sobs at the sight of the glossy mahogany casket in its place. She hid her eyes behind her trembling hands, shouted, almost in anger, "Oh dear God," and quickly began, "The Lord is my shepherd." Strangled by emotion she wept but continued through the psalm, pausing only to swallow tears. "And I will dwell in the house of the Lord forever." Releasing a deep breath, she recited the passage again and again. She would not look at her husband, not now, not today, not tomorrow, not ever again. She prayed, "In Jesus' name."

From just inside the tiny living room, Ralph's mother wouldn't go any closer to her son. She saw his casket, the rose spray, the duty wreaths, and that's all she could take. Held upright by Gertrude and the girls, she retreated to the bedroom where, secluded, they comforted each other, reciting Holy Scripture until the horrid weekend was over.

Saturday's drama continued in the old cotton city of Duluth and the older Shawnee tribal grounds of Suwanee. Two more police funeral motorcades rolled through the county, bringing two more caskets home for two more traumatic ceremonies to begin. Protocol performed in Sugar Hill repeated: state patrol cordoned parking space, six midnight-blue dress uniforms, white gloves, buffed-to-a-gloss leather, polished-to-a-luster metal, and low-stepping cadence thump-clapping against wood floor porches. Police officers Jerry Everett and Jesse Gravitt were home. From Sugar Hill to Suwanee to Duluth, a ten mile route on Highway 23 connected the three open caskets.

Lying in eternal rest, Officer Gravitt had the look of anger and fear frozen on his face, captured by his last vision. A single blood drop stood out on the pillow under his right ear. Stitchwork from the autopsy surrounded his light gray hairline. Although covered by an eyelid, the prosthesis in his right eye fit too low to be unnoticed. Even with a saw-it-coming fearful expression and obvious marks of slaughter, his face still remained defiant, proud, and valiant. Overlooking those qualities, the official dress uniforms numbering in the dozens, the joy of his adored granddaughter playfully dancing over bright yellow tulips outside in the sunlit garden blessed by childlike ignorance of such a sad event, with his Masonic brothers standing strong and the sprays and wreaths and kind-hearted mourners waiting quietly nearby; his mother, Mamie, his wife, Geneva, and the entire Gravitt family gained no comfort from the silver casket centered against the living room wall.

Five miles north, Officer Jerry Everett's body lay underneath a red, white, and blue banner that featured the fifty stars and thirteen stripes of the American flag. Nothing was more deserving of the hallowed cover than a police officer's casket. No other sworn public servant gives more to uphold the country's principles than a police officer. Say what you will, but if you disagree say it to yourself around the Everetts.

Fifteen-year-old Roger, the baby of Carrie and Lee Everett's eight children, saw no end to the column of people dressed in Sunday fineness waiting on the dusty road to pay homage to his brother Jerry. Numbering more than he thought lived in Suwanee, stringing the road for nearly a hundred yards, they passed until fading out of sight below the city water-well pumphouse.

Inside their sparsely furnished home, Jerry's mother and father tearfully admired their sons, George and Kelly who, sharply fitted in their dress blue police uniforms, stood at attention on either side of their brother's body. With only his wife and family in the room, Lee confronted his worst nightmare. He stood over the casket and placed his hands on the flag. Gently folding the stars over the stripes, smoothing the squared crease flat, he admired the gloss finish of the casket.

Ignoring the advice given him earlier by his son's boss, Chief Bell, Lee palmed the lid edge, pushing upward in a slow, trembling motion as if the top weighed a thousand pounds. Bringing it to a stop fully open, he placed his hands on the middle rim. He gripped the ledge, bracing himself for a sight he had never seen, one of his children eternally asleep. Twenty-four hours earlier, this sight was not on his mind. Yesterday morning he'd never thought that the next afternoon would bring this horror. No, yesterday morning he was a man rich from the excesses God had given him: a loving wife, a beautiful family, and a warm home. Today he no longer felt like a rich man.

Lee took in a deep breath. His eyes rolled slowly upward, staring at the ceiling. He drifted off into memories of Jerry as a little boy. Flipping through his mind like a stack of flashcards, he remembered times when the two of them, daily and nightly, annoyed Mama to no end, the times she would rant and how he took her wrath rather than give up the romp. His wife said things such as "Daddy, Jerry needs a fresh diaper!" "Daddy, Jerry needs to eat his cereal." "Daddy, you ain't no pony, set that boy down before you break your back, then you won't be no good to me whatsoever." He'd ignored her in favor of his little boy's laughter. Almost nightly he and his son played hide and seek or tumble-down, loud and well past his bedtime, until a very bothered Carrie shouted, "Hear now, you two! Walter Lee Everett, didn't I tell you half an hour ago to put that boy to bed? Or was you not listening to me, as usual?"

He remembered the time when rather than going to Mr. Moulder's store and coming straight back with the sugar that she sent him to get, he and Jerry accidentally took a three-hour wrong turn, first to the school playground, where Lee pushed his son on the swing set, and then to Devarenn's farm, skipping stones across his drainage pond.

Now, Lee sobbed. A true believer in the gospel, but not always a churchgoer and never much for "Bible reading," still he prayed, "Dear Lord, if I have to beg and crawl the rest of my whole life to take care of my boy, could you please just give me yesterday back?"

His jaws were locked, he gritted his teeth and squinted his eyes. "Dear Almighty God, I swear I'll never ask you for another thing, Oh gracious Lord, if you would just let me have yesterday back."

There was no hope in his prayer. He opened his eyes and summoned all his courage. Lee slowly looked down to his boy's folded hands overlapped above his waist. The sight of his folded hands said it all: this life was gone. Lee sobbed harder, deep sobs. He recalled other years of his boy's life; other Christmases, other birthdays, other Father's Days.

Lee paused at the nameplate pinned above his son's right breast pocket. He read the name, one letter at a time, engraved in the brushed metal. E-V-E-R-E-T-T, his name and the name born to his son. Gripping the casket rim tighter, feeling his legs becoming weaker, his body getting heavier, more years of life passed through his mind. He looked across the jacket to the police badge pinned above his son's left breast pocket. Memories flashed of the time he first saw that badge, the day his boy proudly told him he'd joined the newly formed department.

The half-minute emotional journey reliving cherished moments of Jerry's twenty-eight gone-too-soon years reached an end, one that nothing imagined or warned could have prepared him for what he was about to see, the ghastly mutilated face of his son. His breath stopped, his eyes opened wide and then quickly closed. He lowered his head to his chest and turned away. His knees buckled, and he stumbled. If George and Kelly weren't there to grab him, he would have fallen to the floor.

Taking several deep breaths, he turned toward the sofa behind him. Thinking now of his wife, Lee's heart hurt. This poor woman, the mother of this beautiful boy, the little girl from Barrow County who never had much. How could he let her see her boy, her life, her everything looking like this? *I can't hold her tight enough, wipe her crying eyes dry enough. I have failed her, my boy, and my whole family,* Lee thought.

But from a marriage of forty-plus years, Carrie knew her husband better than he knew himself. She understood what he was putting himself through; his insecurities, a husband and father kind of inadequacy, a self-imposed, unjustified feeling of failure and worthlessness. Always able to comfort him with her courage as only a mother and wife could, she rose from the couch. Smiling through her tears, Carrie hugged Lee and tenderly pulled him into her shoulder.

With strong conviction, she whispered reassuringly, "Daddy, he's not lost. He's with Jesus. Ain't nobody gonna hurt our Jerry now. He's home, Daddy. He waits for us in our Father's house now. We'll be with him again. Someday we'll all be together, and it will be beautiful. Believe in our Lord, Daddy. Believe in what the Bible promises." She sat her husband down in a wood chair beside the casket.

Lifted by the power of her faith, overlooking the horrible wounds inflicted, she turned to view her son. Carrie placed her right hand on top of his chest. Her left hand gently stroked his soft dark hair. She remembered the days of raising her precious little boy, the times she watched him take his awkward first steps. She recalled his skinned knees, and how she blew whistling chords to rid the smarts of the mercurochrome she smeared on his little wounds. She felt foolish remembering how angry she got while mending his only pair of jeans he'd torn from roughhousing with the neighbor boys. How he never cried, not even when his ankle was crushed after he slipped and got caught behind a freight truck backing up to the loading dock where he worked. How she stayed up all night with him, for months, watching him toss in pain from the many surgeries required to pin it together. She remembered her brave little boy smiling through it all, looking at her and saying, "I'll bet ain't nobody ever loved their mama more than I love you." Remembering those words right then, she broke down and inwardly cried, "Oh dear God, what did I ever do to deserve my darling Jerry?"

Closing her eyes, more memories vividly recollected as if it were yesterday. Jerry's childish smile at each birth of his children, two boys and a girl, and his guffawing out loud as he danced down the maternity hall at Joan Glancy Hospital. She wept and the falling teardrops settled in tiny puddles, spotting his proud Everett nametag. Still stroking his hair, she moved her other hand to his forehead. His grotesque appearance had no effect on her adoration for her beautiful son.

She prayed for a short moment before turning to her husband. "Daddy, we gotta let all those folks waiting outside come in and see Jerry. They've been waiting a long time. Thems his friends, our friends. We gotta let them come in, okay?"

Lee, not raising his head, waved for Roger to open the kitchen door.

Standing at attention, a dozen steely-eyed cops formed two cordon lines fixing an order to the home entrance. The long stream of mourners started progressing forward. The lawmen held the hands of visitors, those who needed it, as they went up the plank steps of the side porch and entered the kitchen. The mourners shuffled inside a narrow-roped thruway fronting the policeman's open casket. In steady one-way succession, the uninterrupted stream passed. Most lightly brushed a hand on the folded flag. Many paused, closed their eyes, and said a short prayer. Others simply bowed their heads and kept moving. Some, not acquainted with either the policeman or the Everett family and prompted only by rumors of a gruesome sight, a murder victim riddled by bullets to the head, had come for no other reason than to gawk. They were not disappointed.

Carrie, the ever-courageous matriarch, received everyone with a cordial voice, politely asking for names to unfamiliar faces and telling them, "Thank you for coming. We are so blessed by your presence. Could you please sign the memory book? It would mean so much for us to remember your kind thoughts in our prayers."

After filing past the body, before leaving out the front door, the visitors gave a respectful nod of condolence to the heartbroken father sitting in the wood chair.

Late afternoon, Sunday, April 19, two shiny hearses returned to the homes of Officers Davis and Gravitt. Outside each front door, a police honor guard stood at attention, waiting. The mild sunny day was of no consolation to the somber anguish felt by residents in Duluth and Sugar Hill.

At Jesse Gravitt's home, saddened faces bunched together for a last prayer inside the quiet living room. Jesse's proud Masonic brothers from Norcross Lodge 228 surrounded his casket. Their presence ensured that Brother Gravitt would never be forgotten, that he would be remembered as a humanitarian who enriched many souls with his kindness. The casket lid was closed. The room was cleared. The honor guard moved in. Reversing the order in which he was brought, he was taken away. The roads in Sugar Hill were closed. The hearse motorcade with its police escort had become a mile-long funeral procession. As it rolled away, the long line of cars vanished inside a growing tunnel of dust rising from the dirt road. They arrived at an overflowing Mount Carmel Methodist Church where hundreds of mourners were gathered on the cathedral's front lawn.

Clyde tearfully gazed at his brother one last time before closing the casket. The honor guard marched the body of Officer Davis to the parked hearse and slid it into the carriage bay. Another lengthy procession of cars arrived at one more overflowing church, The First Baptist Church of Sugar Hill.

Each officer was revered. Each was uniquely praised. In addition, Jesse Gravitt was eulogized with a Masonic service followed by an evergreen sprig of acacia placed atop his casket. Both officers were interred with a private graveside service.

Jerry Everett's body remained at his parents' home for a second night, giving out-of-town relatives time to arrive and say a proper goodbye. Monday afternoon one last hearse waited on a dirt road in front of a two-bedroom tin-roof house in Gwinnett County.

Lee and Carrie Everett closed off their home for family only. They gathered in front of their son's casket. His mother clipped a strand of her boy's hair. She stroked the remaining curls back into place as she told him about all the folks who came to pay their respects.

Jerry's father stood at his wife's side and together they said a prayer, again giving thanks for the time God had blessed them with their wonderful little boy. They closed his casket. Lee pulled the flag back in place.

The house cleared, the honor guard walked into the living room, and the police officer's body was taken out the same front door it had been brought in.

The regimen began again, one final time; the marching cadence, the white gloves, the polished leather, the shining badges, and an interminable line of dust-engulfed cars following a hearse, the last of three carrying a policeman's casket through cordoned-off streets in Gwinnett. Police Officer Jerry Everett was given a Full Honors burial at Old Field Baptist Church cemetery. With the report of a twenty-one-gun salute, the saddest three days of ceremonies in Gwinnett County history came to an end.

In all, more than two thousand people turned out to pay tribute to the three slain police officers, but the greatest tribute was given to the people of Gwinnett by the three officers' families who unselfishly opened their homes, allowing a grateful many to pay their last respects.

THE INVESTIGATION

Of Georgia's 159 counties, Gwinnett ranks number fifty in land mass. It is second of metro Atlanta's five, and in 1964 was the state's fourth most populated. For all its lofty rankings, the county still had a small-town feel. Folks either knew everybody or knew somebody who did. Generally those people belonged to one of four groups: the good, the somewhat good, the good for nothing, and the law.

The vast majority of people in Gwinnett were good people, folks who lived by common decency and common sense. They were providers, intent on working together building a better future for themselves, their families, and the county. Although in many ways different, from doctors to ditch diggers, they were all of the same integrity, doing their God-fearing best in whatever they did. To them a civilized society was not at all tolerant of crime.

Aside from the occasional traffic ticket or the more unlikely event of being victimized by crime, they rarely had contact with police. Many even went their entire lives without ever crossing paths with the law.

The somewhat-good group lived in a time still remembered when an extra dollar meant the difference between "young'uns eating or going hungry." A tough bunch, people made their living on the back roads of north Georgia's hill country, a place where making a buck was a "don't care how, just don't get caught" way of life. They were accepted for what they did, providing services and goods to those who had desires. They were people whose dirty laundry, not much and not hidden, was part of Gwinnett's fabric, the same as with many north Georgia counties and all across the Deep South. They were primitive, somewhat shady, altogether unremarkable people. They might run a little shot house, dice table, card game or numbers pool. Maybe they rode a little white lightning down to Atlanta. Maybe a little of this, a little of that, every now and again, "did just whatever it was needed." They weren't criminals per se. Their ranks had dwindled into a fading past, their lives were reformed not by honest ambition but through the process of growing old. Their paths had crossed the law on many occasions, so they had a rapport, a relationship, one of assistance or avoidance, depending on whether victim or perpetrator. Either way, they had mutual respect, a hard-forged friendship formed from years of head-butting. Their past experiences, once gravely serious, became laughable recollections at barbeques and card games regularly enjoyed together. If you had to put a label on them, friend worked just fine. Folks wouldn't give a second thought to sitting beside them in the church pew on Sundays. Preachers hailed them as unnamed subjects in case-in-point sermons claiming "there will be freedom from sin through repentance." Hailed them as well for the coins they pitched in the collection basket, origins of which were never questioned.

The third group was the good for nothings, the hoodlums, robbers, thieves, and thugs. Takers who not once in their miserable lives gave anything back. Punks who'd hoax a few bucks from their own mother and then cry, "To hell with the bitch! That slut ain't nothin but trash no ways." That group used the money for big-shot bragging at penny-ante poker games held in kerosene-soaked supply sheds. They peopled seedy worlds where scumbags got liquored up to acquire self-esteem, conquer their cowardice, and obtain courage. Most came from decent families whose parents didn't raise them to be bums, but from their own stupidity or for whatever convenient reason—usually "someone else's fault," they tripped through life taking one step forward and staggering two steps back. All were lowlife, but a few were mean sons of bitches not to be reckoned with. This group had zero respect for any law or lawman. Their deal was crime, the easier the better. They could not care less if someone got hurt or how much misery came about, and they gave hardly a thought to being busted. Jail time meant little. Going to lockup meant going to a better place.

For every mean criminal, though, there was a meaner, tougher S.O.B. in the county. This brings us to the fourth group, the law, the boys who wore a badge.

They had to be meaner and tougher. In the 1960s if a cop arrested you, he'd simply say, "Shut your mouth, keep it shut, and get in the backseat of that patrol car, now!" Cop cars didn't have protective cages separating the backseat from the front, and usually cops didn't handcuff the bad guys either, because cops didn't use kid gloves. They used brass knuckles. Blackjacks too. These tools were the only ones needed to enforce compliance of "The Rule," "Do exactly what I tell you to do, exactly when I tell you to do it." It was a simple rule, and if followed, all went well. But break "The Rule"—don't comply—and the cop grabbed you by the neck, took out his blackjack, and clocked you over your head until you did.

Understandably those most affected by the murder of three police officers was the law, not just by what had happened, but how it happened. These killings were a wake-up call like never before, and not just for Gwinnett police but for all law enforcement throughout the country. Lawmen took those murders as a clear statement from the bad guys, "If you wear a badge, you wear a target." Cops from Gwinnett, metro Atlanta, and especially the Georgia State Patrol were quick to make a clear statement of their own. "No more Mr. Nice Guy."

The triple homicide redefined the term cold-blooded murder and became the benchmark for training officer safety. Police academies formed using hard-ass veteran cops as instructors. Self-defense tactics were taught with emphasis on disarming a bad guy who had the drop on an officer. Recurrent training became mandatory with a passing grade required before the officer could return to patrol duty.

Instructors drilled tactics into officers throughout their training, "If somebody beats you to the draw, for God's sake, come what may, don't ever give up your gun!"

Officers were also taught, "Use your intuition. Always have a mindset for safekeeping." First and foremost, "Whatever goes, make sure it's you who goes home at shift's end." They were told, "Do whatever's necessary. Better we worry about the details later than not at all." A close second, "Trust nobody. It doesn't matter if it's your worst enemy or best friend that kills you, you'll still be dead. Leave your trust in the locker." Third, "Don't ever turn your back to anybody. It doesn't matter if you're writing a parking ticket or making an arrest, maintain eye contact with your subject at all times." Lastly, "Take control of every situation. Your duty is to protect and serve. You can't do that unless you're the one who's in control." Patrol commanders instructed their officers, "Take nothing for granted. Always expect the worst, be prepared to stop it, and make sure you've got a back-up plan."

For cops on the street guidelines for applying "The Rule" had broadened. Who could blame them? Newspaper headlines read, "Three cops handcuffed, marched into woods, murdered."

Policing—not just in some big city's filth pit but also in rural counties—became a deadly game that lawmen either had what it took to play in, or if not, turn in their badge.

After watching three equals lowered into graves, several police officers quit. Stirred with a strong sense of urgency to settle the score, most officers stayed on. After returning home from their buddies' funerals, they removed the .38 from their gun belt and holstered a .357 magnum. Those who remained probably gritted their teeth and vowed, "If that's the way they want it, that's the way they're gonna get it."

 co

The seldom-traveled dirt lane known as Arc Road cut through land locals knew as Guthrie Farm and was surrounded by thick woods, narrow paths, and slow-moving creeks. It was an ideal habitat for deer and small game. As long as anyone could remember, hunters had tromped

through these woods littering its brush with spent cartridge casings of every caliber. The serene starlit nights
also made Arc a popular refuge for teenage frolic. Empty
beer cans and whiskey bottles told of their visits.

Saturday morning at first light more than a dozen
lawmen returned to Arc Road to search for evidence they
might have missed the day before. Of utmost impor-
tance, they wanted to find the three missing guns to veri-
fy if they were, in fact, the murder weapons. Maybe they
would get lucky, lift some fingerprints, maybe even the
killers' prints. Measured against the previous day's disappointment they, for certain, had nothing to lose.

Sitting on their front porch, A. C. Mills and his wife
Ruby watched as lawmen again walked up and down Arc
Road sweeping through the dirt with their boots. Count,
the Mills' Weimaraner, ran back and forth in "his" front
yard barking at the men on "his" road. The Mills' split-lev-
el brick house stood in the center of a treeless two-acre lot
one hundred feet from the right side of Arc Road, a quarter mile up from Arc's south entrance off Beaver Ruin.
The house faced west, the same direction from where the
winds blew. With a mix of Arc's dust, April's thick pine
pollen, and the night's heavy dew, their sunbaked home
was covered in a dirty yellow crust. More dirt churned
from the road whenever a car or truck passed, and carried by the incoming wind, another layer of red Georgia
clay dusted the house. The weathered narrow road continued past the house uphill gradually for another eighth
of a mile before topping out and then falling from view
over the opposite side. Mr. Mills, Carl to his friends, was
the only eyewitness to the late-night crime, sort of. The
eighty-year-old country boy had some time before lost
his better health. Mostly homebound, he took medica-
tion for his ailing heart, wore thick glasses for his failing

eyesight and, except for Count's thunderous bark and Ruby's call for dinner, had little to no hearing.

The new morning sun replenished the open country's splendor, returning Arc Road to its natural purity. A. C. Mills stood in his front yard a few short steps from the dirt road edge. Count now sat quietly by his side. Detectives, desperate for information, talked with the elderly gentleman about what he recalled from two nights before.

Mills told them, "I guess it was something just after twelve thirty, thereabouts. We'd been sleeping for a good little while till this dog woke us with his barking. Don't normally, but I got out of bed to see what had him all bothered. I seen out the window..." Mills points with an unsteady finger. "They's two cars parked this side of that hilltop up there, one right in behind the other. Then I seen a man sorta walking around."

The city detectives, anticipating a revelation, peered in close toward the old man.

"Dog was still with his ruckus, so I telephoned the sheriff's office. Tell you what I told that radio man. Ain't supposed to be no cars out here that time of night." Mills' agitation sparked, recalling the conversation. "I told y'all I don't know how many times y'all call yourselves the damn law. Hell, don't none of y'all care nothing 'bout us."

The detectives stared at each other, shrugged, and then stepped back to their original positions.

"Something right close to...maybe one o'clock... could be more, could be less...y'all show up." He pointed. "From that other side over yonder. Well, the one what was parked in back come down here." Mills recaptured the moment with a frantic look wrinkled in his forehead. "Backwards! Right here in front of my house, then here y'all come...got your flashing lights going. Done something till the both of yah leave......you first...up that hill there." Mills stared up Arc Road's long rise. "They's all out in the road, walking, smoking cigarettes, looked like to me. Stayed maybe ten minutes or so, whenever their lights come on. Then off they went over the other side."

Mills tired. He took a long deep breath. "I hadn't seen nothing else till, I figure, twenty minutes later, when I seen yawl's police car again. Come back over that hill going past here like there weren't no tomorrow." Mills pointed in the direction of Beaver Ruin. Count followed with his eyes as if to confirm his master's story. "They come through down there. Don't hardly stop. Gone off to somewheres, I don't know. Northeast expressway, I reckon."

The detectives stared in bewilderment at Mills.

"Police car?"

"Yeah. Told my wife, 'There goes that police car.' Told her I figured must be everything's fine now."

"That's it? Everything's fine now?"

"Yeah! Said maybe now this boy will shut up. Get us some sleep. Way I seen it, figured it was all over with. Now if y'all was to ask me any more to what I know, I'll tell you that's all I know. Didn't hear no gun shooting, didn't know nothing more than what I just told ya. I know now, but not then, nothing 'bout them polices got killed." The proud country gentleman and his devoted guardian nodded together, "No, sir. Terrible!"

"And your wife?"

"What about her? She didn't see nothing."

Taking everything into consideration: Mills' overall health, his angry mood, his sleepless agitation, and the excitement of watching a police car chase; the pitch-black hour of night; and the pollen-crusted windows; lawmen discounted Mills as a credible witness. Except for his vague memory of time and duration, they believed his recollection was not worth the twenty minutes they spent hearing it. From the tire imprints found on Arc, detectives had already reasoned the movement of the cars and the sequence of events that took place that night. Obviously with the police car having been found parked in the woods, Mills' claim of watching it speed past his house to Beaver Ruin could not have possibly happened.

One frustrated lawman raised his voice to the others as they walked from Mills' front yard heading back up Arc Road's long hill, "Good Lord, if the old man can't recognize a cop car a few minutes after seeing it in front of his own damn face, then hell, he didn't see a goddamn thing at all."

After another full day of looking through and beyond the litter, spent cartridge casings, empty beer cans, and whiskey bottles, and finally talking with their only eyewitness, Saturday's search yielded the same as it did the day before. Nothing. Not a clue. Again lawmen left Arc Road no better off for leads than when they came.

While walking his dog Sunday afternoon, a local boy spotted something shiny in the drainage ditch along Beaver Ruin Road. Bobby Tidwell discovered what lawmen had spent all weekend looking for. Fifteen feet off the right side of the road, a quarter mile west of Arc Road, Officer Everett's nickel-plated .38 special lay half buried in the dirt. Bobby called the sheriff's office to report the find.

On their way home from attending both Officer Davis' and Gravitt's funerals, GBI Agent H. B. Freeman, riding with State Trooper M. J. Vandiver and Gwinnett Investigator Fred Banks, received a radio call from the jailhouse. Told of the discovery, the three lawmen drove to Beaver Ruin Road where they found a wide-grinning young boy waving their State Patrol car to a stop. Agent Freeman, a large-framed, hard-faced Gwinnett resident distraught over the death of his three friends, exited the car. Neither amused nor charmed by the boy's joyful smile, he asked, "You the one who called in about finding a gun?"

Excited to have the lawman's attention, Bobby exclaimed, "Yes, sir! I seen it first."

"Did you pick it up or touch it in any way?"

"No, sir. Didn't touch it in no way. Just stood over it is all."

Freeman continued, "Where is it, son? Show me."

Bobby walked off the road stepping several feet into the shallow ditch. He pointed toward the ground several more feet in front of where he stood.

Vandiver, tall, lanky, dressed spotlessly in his blue, heavily starched State Patrol uniform shouted, "I see it! That's Jerry's gun, nickel, bone handle. I'd know that gun from a mile away."

Freeman stared toward the expressway. "The others are gonna be around here close. Fred, how 'bout we go up—hold on, looks like a flashlight over there. Damn. Stanley pegged it, said they'd have thrown 'em out before going too far."

Banks said, "Yeah, bastards probably heading for the expressway."

"Fred, we're what, how far you figure we're up from Arc Road?"

"My guess would be about a quarter mile or so."

Freeman looked at young Bobby. "Son, which way you come from?"

"Come from my house, not much farther past Arc."

"You didn't see any other guns or flashlights down that way, did you?"

"No, sir."

"You figure you'd a seen 'em if they were?"

"Oh yes, sir, figure I would've. Don't think I'd a missed 'em."

"Well," Freeman said, "I appreciate your help, son. Go on home now and leave us to our business." The burly agent called out, "Fred, let's you and me walk up here where I'll bet we find the others. Trooper, how 'bout you bag and mark that gun then come with us?"

Feeling more important than shy, young Bobby wore a wily smile as he asked the heavyset officer, "Excuse me, sir, if y'all find any more guns and all, and thems the ones what belonged to those dead cops, well, I know that a bunch of yawls been looking for 'em, and I'm the one who found 'em and all, so do I get some kind of reward money?"

To somber Agent H. B. Freeman the new No More Mr. Nice Guy came naturally. "Boy, I just come from… reward money you're asking for, huh? Look here, boy! I just come from two funerals, funerals for two of them dead cops, them being Officer Davis and Officer Gravitt to you. Just right now, you done caught me in a bad way. What I really ought to do is carry your little ass back to the jailhouse, let you sit in one of those cells for…oh…I don't know, maybe a few days. Ain't nobody gonna give a shit if I do, 'cause see, I could hold you for that long under suspicion it was you who put this gun here. That's accessory to a crime! But since you asked, I'm gonna give you a reward all right." An angry Freeman stared close in to the young boy's face. "How 'bout instead of me slamming your sorry little ass in that patrol car, hauling you off to jail, I let you go back to whatever rock it was you crawled out from under, and boy, I got a feeling you're gonna take that reward and get. Right now!"

With his face turned pale white, Bobby replied to the angry agent, "Yes, sir. Thank you."

After a twenty-minute search the lawmen found another flashlight and the other two officers' guns spread out fifty yards apart along the roadside ditch.

Agent Freeman said, "M. J., get 'em all over to Doc Howard's lab. And get hold of Stanley. Let him know what's going on. Tell him looks to me like they was bailing out of here pretty good, the way everything's was spaced out. I'm sure somebody was chucking 'em out as fast as he could. Probably want to check and see if any tickets got wrote up Thursday night. Maybe we'll get lucky the sons of bitches got caught speeding. You never know."

***

Monday morning in downtown Atlanta, Dr. Larry Howard, irritable, arrived at the GBI crime lab. His assistant, Paul Serene, greeted him. "Morning, Doc. Say, tell me, what in the world happened up there in Gwinnett Friday?"

"I'm sure you've heard. It's been all over the news and in the papers. You know how to read, don't you?"

"Oh Jesus, I can see you're in one of those moods today. Yeah, I know how to read, Larry, but believing is another thing."

"I'm sorry, Paul. It's just I'm as tired as ever I can remember. I haven't gotten much sleep these last few days thinking about it. Jesus, I don't want to think about it. I can't imagine what was going through those boys' minds there at the end, staring down a gun barrel. God Almighty!" Howard shook his head. "All I could think about was those poor families. Try putting yourself in their place."

"I don't believe I can, Larry, I don't believe anybody can."

"I'll tell you this much, it was a bad day for our boys up there. As bad as it can get."

"Isn't that the God's truth? And they were hand-cuffed?"

"Yeah, hell, they were slaughtered, all three, just slaughtered."

"That's insane! Who in their right mind would do something like that?"

"You've answered your own question. Nobody in their right mind would. I thought I'd seen it all in this business, but I guess not. Certainly not anything like that. Paul, I swear you never know what the day's gonna bring."

"No, I guess not. Listen, Lieutenant Stanley brought in the guns yesterday."

"The officers' guns? He found the officers' guns?"

"Yeah, found them yesterday afternoon beside Beaver Ruin. Said they were just up from that dirt road where you were."

"Finally some good news. Where are they?"

"Got 'em, and a couple of flashlights on the bench in back. Told the lieutenant we'd start on them as soon as you got in. I guess you've heard Jim and Captain Hutchins are running lead on this thing."

"Well, I knew Jim would be, but Arthur, no, I haven't heard that." Howard expressed his concerns. "I will say this, though. As good as those two are, they've got a damn tough row to hoe. Let's see what we can do to help get 'em started."

Inside their crammed hand-built crime lab Howard and Serene began examining the guns. First labeled by serial number, they would later be individually identified by members of the slain officers' families.

All three guns were four-inch barrel, six-shot, .38 caliber Smith and Wesson 'model 10' police revolvers. Officers Everett's and Gravitt's guns were chambered for the slightly more powerful .38 special cartridge. In its cylinder, Everett's plated steel revolver held a total of two empty bullet casings of the same make and caliber as the live rounds found on his gun belt. Howard presumed the casings were pulled from the two empty bullet slots he saw on the back of Everett's holster belt. Although no spent casings found at the crime scene matched the two in the gun cylinder or looped to his belt, the examiners assumed Everett carried the gun fully loaded. Officer Gravitt's blue service revolver held six spent .38 special rounds. Officer Davis' older model blue .38 held five spent casings with one live round, hammer struck but failed to fire.

Partial fingerprints lifted from the weapons proved to be only those of the three officers. No other prints were found. In all, Howard believed a total of nineteen shots had been fired, hitting the policemen a combined sixteen times. Davis and Gravitt five times each; Officer Everett, six times. Many of the soft lead bullets recovered during the autopsies, plus those dug from the dirt underneath the policemen at the crime scene, were too mutilated to be identified; however, ballistic tests positively identified three of the five rounds from the ground plus several bullets taken from the bodies as having been fired through the three retrieved guns. There was no doubt the officers were murdered by bullets fired from their own service revolvers.

☙

During the next several weeks more than twenty pounds of charred remnants combed out of the burned Oldsmobile interior, fingerprints taken from the patrol car, shoe and tire molds taken on Arc Road, debris ranging from matchbook covers to empty liquor bottles, and all bits and pieces that had been crammed inside paper bags or rolled up in blankets at the crime scene received full forensic examination at the lab. Although every item was either photographed using infrared cameras, dusted, smoked for prints or compared to similar items confiscated from suspects, no item, not one, was ever linked or established as evidential to the crime.

Because the Oldsmobile had been stolen out of DeKalb County, investigation of the burned vehicle came under the jurisdiction of DeKalb police department's Vice Division commanded by their lead detective, Lieutenant John Crunkleton. With permission granted by Gwinnett authorities, DeKalb Police Chief Brady Knight was given authority to investigate the case inside Gwinnett County lines.

The Saturday night following the murders, Chief Knight called Lieutenant Crunkleton. "John, what you got so far on the burned Oldsmobile up there in Gwinnett?"

Crunkleton responded, "It's out of here, Briarcliff and Lavista. Talked with the owner, who saw it last around ten thirty Thursday night. Local boys from up there got it."

"How do you know it was local boys?"

"Nobody but locals would know that dirt road."

"What else do you know about our friends up there?"

"I know a few places, but not much for names."

"Anybody here does?"

"Yeah, Homer Lee Cheek, sheriff's office, he knows a good bit about who's up there."

"Okay, here's what let's do. I want you on this thing day and night. You'll have free reign in Gwinnett. I've already made the arrangements. I'll call Sheriff Frazier and get Mr. Cheek. I don't want another black stripe on this badge. Hear me? You gotta know that when you find the car thieves, you'll find the killers. They'll be expecting you to come. Do whatever's needed. I'll cover for you every inch of the way, just get this thing wrapped up like yesterday ain't quick enough. You got that?"

"Yeah, I got it."

Chief Knight called Sheriff Frazier. Fuming with anger he hollered, "Goddamnit, Harold, three of our officers. Those sons of bitches! The burned Olds on that dirt road came from here. It's ours, Harold, and I want this one real bad. I'm putting Lieutenant John Crunkleton on this thing full time. I've got Chief Bell's say so, but I'm gonna need your help."

"That right?"

"Yeah, that's right, Harold. Crunkleton knows a few places up there but not names. He says Homer Lee Cheek does."

"Yeah, Brady, I believe that would be true. I also believe I know where you're going with this. Cheek, as you know, is my best detective, and at this time he has his hands full working for me."

"I want those bastards, Harold! Hell, that dirt road ain't but six miles from here. I don't want those goddamn sons of bitches coming down here. Least not alive, I don't."

"I might be able to persuade Cheek to team up with Crunkleton. Of course he's gonna have to drop everything he's doing, which means I'm gonna be short-handed for a while."

"Don't be an ass to me, Harold!"

"Easy, Chief, we're on the same side. I'll tell ya, I'm madder than a wet hornet, same as you."

"Sheriff, never in my lifetime have I wanted anything more than to see whoever done this hang. Hanged and burned!"

"Yes, sir. Seems to me, Chief, that'd be fit and proper, I do believe. Between Homer Lee and John you'll get your wish. We both will, I want 'em just as bad or more than you do. I'll have Cheek call the lieutenant tonight. If I know him, he's gonna jump all over this thing with both feet."

"Harold, I'm taking this thing real personal."

"I can tell, and I'd say that'd be all right."

❧

On Monday morning detectives Crunkleton and Cheek met at the Gwinnett County City Hall to begin their investigation. Driving in Crunkleton's unmarked car, their first stop was Red Ledford's gas station in Buford. Cheek pointed out the window. "John, looky here at who I'm seeing. That's M. C. Perry, local boy I've busted many a time. Got a felony sheet ten years running. Pull over. I'm gonna have a little talk with him, see what he knows."

Well known by North Georgia law enforcement, twenty-six-year-old Marion Calvin Perry was a criminal more proficient at getting caught than eluding police. Having already served seven years behind bars, a good portion on county chain gangs, Perry had not a care in the world for making an honest living or the likely consequence of getting caught. He shrugged off apprehension as a risk he took to play his game. Incarceration was never a deterrent to his criminal behavior. His philosophy: "I gotta somehow make a living. The law's got a job to do. Ain't no need taking offense to that."

The car tires scrubbed through the parking lot gravel until it came to a stop. Cheek, a burly country lawman of unshakable repute, hollered out the open window, "M. C. Perry, hold it right there, boy. I want to talk with you."

Perry sat on top of the ice cream freezer drinking a bottle of Coke. "If it ain't Detective Homer Lee Cheek. You a long ways from home, ain't ya, Mr. Cheek? What ya doing up here?"

Cheek, with a determined stride, walked to Perry. "Boy, come down off that box. Stand up on your damn feet when you talk to me."

"Yes, sir."

"Where was you last Thursday night, M. C.?"

"Let me think on that for a minute. Oh yeah, my granddaddy's place, Dahlonega."

"Got folks up there who'll vouch for that?"

"Bunch, yes, sir. This about those polices, ain't it?"

"What do you know about it, M. C.?"

"What I read in the papers is all. Well, heard too, what they had on the news."

"That right?" The detective towered over Perry. "Listen to me real good, M. C., 'cause I ain't gonna beat around the bush. Did you have anything to do with it?"

"No, sir!" Perry's face flushed.

"Nothing about it?"

"Nothing about it."

"Who would've?"

"Mr. Cheek, I have no idea. All I know is like I'm telling ya. I ain't had nothing' to do with it."

"M. C., you knew them officers didn't ya?"

"Yes, sir, I knew Jerry Everett. Know'd Ralph Davis too."

"You heard there was a stolen car? Stolen Oldsmobile found burned at the scene. You know that?"

"It was all over the papers. Television too. Sure I did."

"Did you have anything to do with that car, M. C.?"

"Mr. Cheek, I already told you, I don't know nothing about that car or them polices getting killed. Only thing I know is I ain't had nothing to do with any of it."

"Sixty-three Oldsmobile, two-door hardtop?"

"Don't mean nothing to me."

"All right, I'll be talking with you soon. Stay where I can get hold of you, hear?"

"Oh, I hear you. Ain't gonna be hard to find neither, 'cause I'm turning in next week, on that liquor charge. You can come see me any ol' time you feel. Federal pen in Atlanta, that's where I'll be for the next two years."

"Yeah boy, I'm sure of that." Cheek turned toward the car.

Perry raised his head with surprise, "Whoa, whoa, wait a minute."

Cheek turned back. "Something else, M. C.?"

"Yeah, maybe there is. Let me think about it. Yeah, now I remember. I might know something, something you want to know."

"Tell me, boy!"

Perry, looking cocky, said, "Well now, let's talk a little bit first, Mr. Cheek."

"Boy, I ain't got no time for your little punk-ass games! Tell ya what let's do. How 'bout you come get in the car with me. We'll take us a quick ride. Wanna do that?"

"No, sir."

"Then talk!"

"Yes, sir. About two weeks ago, Venson Williams called me, said he was looking for an Oldsmobile. You know Venson Williams?"

"Yeah, go on."

"Well, like I was saying, Williams called me, asked me to be on the lookout for an Oldsmobile. I told him

I wasn't interested in working with him on account he never did pay up money he owes me."

"Owes you money? For what?"

"Just some money he owes me, that's all."

"Okay, and he said what?"

"That's pretty much all there was to it. We just hung up."

Cheek, with his lawman's intuition said, "That right? Hmm." The detective looked down at Perry's boots and then slowly raised his gaze to Perry's eyes. "But there's something else you ain't telling me, huh?"

"Yeah, then, well, 'bout three days later, Alex Evans called me, said he was looking for a sixty-three Olds like you're talking about, two-door hardtop."

"That right? Why would Evans call you?"

"Cause he said he knew everything...the way I felt 'bout Williams. Said if I got this car, this sixty-three Olds, it was him I'd be getting it for. Wouldn't be getting it for Williams."

"Why?"

"Well, I guess him and Williams was in on it together."

"Was Evans offering you any money?"

"Yes, sir, a hundred dollars."

"Did you look for that car?"

"No, sir. Laughed at him. Said, 'Hell, Alex, I could steal one for myself, make a whole lots more than a hundred dollars. Shit, I can get three, four hundred dollars on my own.' Didn't need him in on something like that. If I was gonna do any car stealing, which I ain't."

"What did Evans say to that?"

"Told me I could make good money doing maybe a handful or more cars a week working for him."

"That right?"

"Yes, sir. Said all I had to do was get the cars and bring 'em directly. He'd pay me the moment I got out of the car. Said, 'Easy money.'"

"Easy money, huh? And you said?"

"I already done told you, Mr. Cheek. Told him I could make four more times that kind a money doing it for myself. Didn't need him."

"Tell me again when those conversations took place."

"Venson, he called me 'bout two weeks ago, maybe ten days, I don't remember exactly. And Alex, he called me week after that, maybe early part of week past."

"A week before the murders?"

"Yes, sir, be about right."

"They didn't tell you why they were looking for a sixty-three Olds two-door hardtop, in specific?"

"No, sir, just that, is all."

"Okay M. C., I'm sure I'll speak with you again on this."

"Mr. Cheek, Alex and Venson...well, they ain't gonna be too happy 'bout what I told you. Can you maybe do something for me on this stretch I'm fixing to ride?"

"Fed time, M. C.? Can't help you with no Fed time. That'd be your little red wagon to pull."

"Yes, sir, I just thought that maybe..."

The no-nonsense detective stood determined over M. C. "Boy, I'm gonna ask you once more, and right now would be the time you come clean. Did you have anything to do with killing those officers?"

"I ain't never killed nobody, Mr. Cheek, and I didn't have nothing to do with killing them officers. No, sir, I did not!"

"We'll see 'bout that, M. C. Sure will."

Cheek returned to the parked car where Crunkleton waited. "Homer Lee, looked like you was getting on him pretty good. What'd he say?"

"John, you're not gonna believe this, but our little bird just sang. Hit us pay dirt. Alex Evans and Venson Williams."

Just three days after the crime, not yet one full day into their investigation, the detectives had indeed hit pay dirt. For most of his adult life Venson Eugene Williams had worked as an attendant and mechanic at several used car lots in metro Atlanta. By 1964, he'd built an impressive resume of documented criminal activity. The thirty-four-year-old Williams had served time for auto theft, carrying a concealed weapon, and felon in possession of a firearm. But for his criminal past, Williams, married and father of three, came across as "the boy next door," according to neighbors in the west Atlanta suburb where he lived. On the night of the police murders, Venson Williams was free on arraignment bond while awaiting trial on a federal charge of conspiracy for the hijacking of an interstate tractor-trailer loaded with bonded red liquor.

Had it not been for M. C. Perry's divulgence, Venson Williams' name most likely would not have made the initial list of suspects.

Alex Evans, however, most definitely would have. From day one his name occupied the top spot on that list. Thirty-eight year-old Buford resident Alex S. Evans was married with three children and not your ordinary suspect. In a place and time when country boys slopped around in heavy denim and muddy boots, Evans dressed his six-foot, two-inch frame in sport jackets, starched cotton shirts, pressed trousers, and shined leather shoes. He was already an intimidating figure in stance, but his face took on an even more sinister look with his eyes shadowed underneath the turned-down brim of his porkpie hat. Alex had two completely different personalities, both genuine, both easily switched back and forth. One moment he could be the nicest guy you'd ever met, charming, educated, and polished. Especially good at "nice talk," he'd converse with anyone on any subject. A moment later, he could be a conniving, manipulative swindler not beyond brutality to have it his way, and when he wanted it his way, Alex cared for no one else but Alex.

Depending on their relationship with Evans, most folks saw only one or the other of his two personalities, but the law officers, who knew him best, saw both. In fact, they knew him on a personal level. From 1956 to 1962, he was one of their own. For six years Alex Evans wore a badge. His first was as a Federal Revenue Agent, but during his probation period Evans was released by the department when someone discovered errors on his application. He had lied to get the job.

A thin, sometimes hostile line between law enforcement and the media made it almost certain that firing a badge would bring on the prying eyes of newspaper weasels digging for a crooked cop story. This might expose occasional illicit tactics lawmen had to use for outwitting bad guys.

To avoid attention, undesirables were quietly passed off from one agency to another, usually as an "I know what you're doing but we'll look the other way and keep this our little secret." A secret was whatever the passing agency used as a bargaining chip for the favor's return. "Take this guy off my hands, and we'll call it square." Beyond the news weasels' knowledge, this pact included a handy bridge for transferring a problem cop away from an enough-is-enough fed-up commander. "He's no longer my problem; let the next guy deal with him." Such was the case with Alex Evans.

Believing he'd tried to hoodwink them, the federal revenuers passed Evans off to the Georgia Department of

Revenue, where he became a field agent snooping back road mash factories in the state's northeast territory. Evans twisted feelings of insult into opportunity. "I'll show the bastards just who the hell they're messing with." He took full advantage of the transfer, using his badge to build a "my way or else" co-op with moonshiners. For three years his network of mash makers grew until finally the state got wise and Alex Evans was again handed a one-way ticket across the "bridge."

This time he was moved to the Gwinnett County Sheriff's Department, and the state informed the new sheriff, the biggest still owner in the county, "You've got yourself a new deputy coming." Familiar with Evans, though reluctant to oblige, the sheriff had no choice but to accept the deal. Besides, with all his jailhouse improprieties and the secrets the state held over him, going against the wishes of the revenue boys in downtown Atlanta was a fight he wasn't going to win. The sheriff politely accepted his new hire and quickly realized the transfer was a good fit for his own enterprise. From three years of scouring through the state's northeast woods, Evans knew where to find the mash, and where one finds the mash, one finds the sheriff's competition.

Raiding and destroying stills gave the sheriff a corner on the market while at the same time kept him in good graces with the Revenue boys. But after two years of complaints, such that he'd never have believed until one night seeing it firsthand, Evans had to go. Calling Evans a coward, liar, and thug, the sheriff fired Evans for, of all things, abusing a prisoner he'd arrested for drunkenness. Firing his moonshining partner presented a big risk to his business and office, but the sheriff so despised his deputy that any personal loss didn't much matter anymore. The sheriff's jig was already up. The Feds were closing in on his jailhouse operation. They were going to bust him soon, and he knew it.

For Evans, the humiliating slide down law enforcement's ladder didn't settle well with either his ego or his wallet. He'd gone from a 700-dollar-a-month suit-wearing agent to a 200-dollar-a-month uniformed deputy, but the six-year slide down the cop ladder gave him the smarts to climb up the criminal ladder. By 1964, Evans knew more about crime in Gwinnett than anyone else in the county. He had his hand in all the rackets: car thievery, cosmetics, furniture, gambling, home appliances, moonshine, tires, tools, whatever. If a tractor-trailer load of hot goods entered Gwinnett, he'd know about it, and if he got involved with it, he knew where to fence the merchandise. After his release from the sheriff's department, for a man having no visible means of supporting himself, Alex lived a rich life. He had a lavishly furnished home, a fat pocket roll of money, and expensive clothes. The grip of a .38 snub-nosed revolver stuck out from his belt and a fully loaded M1 carbine rode alongside him in the passenger seat of his 1950 Ford two-door hotrod coupe. At the time of the murders Alex Evans was free on bond while appealing his federal conviction for illegally manufacturing and distributing distilled liquor, a conviction he shared with his old boss, the former Gwinnett County Sheriff.

❧

Tuesday morning, four days after the murders, GBI Director Major Barney Ragsdale called a meeting at the Lawrenceville City Hall for law officers working to solve the triple homicide. Sitting in with Ragsdale were GBI Assistant Director Captain Arthur Hutchinson, who in 1938 became the first agent appointed to the new GBI and was considered the state's best homicide investigator; Colonel Lowell Connor, appointed by Governor Carl Sanders as Georgia's public safety director and commander of the Georgia State Patrol; GBI Lieutenant James Stanley; State Trooper M. J. Vandiver; Gwinnett County Police Chief J. O. Bell; Gwinnett Solicitor Reid Merritt; and DeKalb County police detectives John Crunkleton and Homer Lee Cheek.

Ragsdale addressed the group, "Y'all already know each other, so let's get started. Dr. Howard tells me there are no prints on the guns, on the patrol car, on anything. I'm afraid we're not gonna get any help from the lab on this one. Anybody got anything?"

Homer Lee Cheek said, "Two names. Got 'em yesterday from M. C. Perry up in Buford: Alex Evans and Venson Williams."

"What did Perry say?"

"Said for the last couple weeks Evans and Williams been asking him to find a sixty-three Olds, same as our Olds on Arc Road."

Ragsdale responded, "Well, I wouldn't be surprised if Evans was involved. I know Williams too, but Evans, that doesn't surprise me at all. What Perry said, then that same car showing up on Arc Road, that's no coincidence. What else you got?"

"That's all for right now. I believe what he says, and that's good enough for me."

"Hardly! We can't get a conviction on hearsay, certainly not from the likes of M. C. Perry. We're gonna need a whole lot more than that, but it's a very good start."

Hutchins piped up. "Barney, about this fella Perry, I don't think it's coincidence what he told Homer Lee. That Oldsmobile is in the middle of this thing. It wasn't a random take; it was a target. Lieutenant Crunkleton figures they're local boys. I agree. They were familiar with that dirt road, they planned on being there, but I don't believe they planned on being there long. I think their intent wasn't stripping the car but rather changing the car tag and driving off. Our officers must have driven up and somehow, they got the drop put on 'em. That road gets dark out there at night, pitch black dark. Even if you're fully alert it wouldn't matter. Anybody can jump you in the dark. The murders were probably secondary to the car theft. It was purely a result of being in the wrong place at the wrong time. As far as motive is concerned, somebody or bodies knew one another. Recognition was the reason they were killed."

Ragsdale recoiled. "Killed like that? Over a stolen car? They'd do that?"

"Hell, Major, you kidding me?" Hutchins said. "Damn right they'd do it! I've seen it for a lot less. You have too. Felony auto theft will get a man two years in state prison. Throw a little bad blood in the mix, and guns will go bang."

Reid Merritt spoke, "Major, I can put a tap on Evans' phone. Can't use it for prosecution, but it might be worth pursuing."

Ragsdale paused. "Lieutenant Stanley, would you like to give us any thoughts on that?"

"Yeah, well, I'll tell you this much. I'm not surprised hearing Evans' name. That crazy screwball has a mind warped enough to kill. Hell, he's been a loaded cannon for years. Good shoe prints in the dirt says we got three perps. Evans and Williams makes two. Question is, who's the third? Might be a good idea to tap his phone. Maybe we'll find out. Got nothing to lose from trying."

Ragsdale turned to Cheek. "What about your boy, Perry? Could he be the third man?"

"Nope, Perry's got an out. Checked on it this morning. He wasn't there."

Crunkleton shook his head. "Somebody besides Perry knows something. Me and Homer Lee are gonna turn this county upside down till we find out who."

Merritt said, "John, keep me up to date with...no, on second thought, let me go along when you're interrogating your suspects. You too, Arthur. Now that we've got names, let's make sure we do this by the book. It'll give me the chance to lay out a prosecution. Major Ragsdale, John, Homer Lee, do any of you have a problem with that?"

Ragsdale spoke up, "I think that's a good idea. Maybe some of us could learn a thing or two along the way."

Hutchins rubbed his face. "Something tells me there's a missing link here somewhere. Why else this particular sixty-three Oldsmobile? And this third man? It's all connected. Crunkleton, you know what to look for. Somewhere out there is a sixty-three Oldsmobile, sitting in somebody's shop."

Ragsdale looked at a very somber, stone-faced Chief Bell. "Chief? Anything you want to say?"

"No, Major, y'all boys got this, not me. Though I'm thinking like the rest, wouldn't hold it past Alex Evans' doings. No sir, not at all. Matter of fact we've all been wondering about him ourselves."

"Wondering about him?" Ragsdale asked. "How's that?"

Chief Bell commented, "Hadn't seen him lately. Just seems a might strange to me."

"Why?"

"Well, Alex, he knew my boys real good. I'd say they were good friends. Matter of fact, Jerry and Ralph would go over to his house for dinner once or twice a week.

Cooked dinner on his grill at night. I haven't seen him since this happened. Nobody I've talked with has seen him. Not at the funerals or for that matter anywhere, and it ain't from not looking either. That boy didn't go to a single funeral, and that just doesn't seem...well, just seems real funny him not being around at a time like that. Suspicious, you ask me. I mean, he rode with 'em when he was a deputy. Makes my stomach turn thinking it was him pulled the trigger on those boys, knowing each of 'em the way he did." Chief Bell slumped in his chair, shaking his head. "Looking those boys in their faces and then killing 'em like that. Let him rot in hell if he done it."

Merritt was quick to comment, "Chief Bell, I can certainly understand your anguish, and I can't say I blame you, but at this point, all we have are two names. As Major Ragsdale said earlier, we can't go on the hearsay of just one man. Adjudication of this crime will depend on real evidence. Gentlemen, our views of Evans won't mean a tinker's damn in a court of law, and I think it appropriate that we not show any bias toward him or any other person at this time, not until we have specific, concrete evidence pointing to a guilty party. As much as anyone in this room, I too want justice for those three officers, but only to the extent the law allows, not through the sight of a lynch mob. This is for all of you here. We must proceed without prejudice and let the cards fall where they may."

"Gentlemen, please listen to what Mr. Merritt says," Hutchins said. "Now, everyone here knows Evans. Probably feel he's capable of doing this, probably feel he's involved, but let's not broadcast our feelings outside this room. We've got to be quiet, not show our hand, certainly not to Williams, and especially not to Evans. If I know anything at all about him, if he did in fact do this, he's covered his bases. Wouldn't leave much behind for clues,

I'm sure. And I can almost guarantee you, if he finds out we're on his trail, he'll skate, making it all the harder for us to bag him. That is, again, if he's guilty. I understood what you said, Mr. Merritt."

"All right, let's get it figured out," said Ragsdale. "I'll be central on this. Copy me in on what y'all are doing. I need to know. Gentlemen, there's one other thing I want to say before we get out of here. My telephone has been ringing off the hook these last few days. Those goddamn ink slingers down at that Journal news-paper has got everybody in a fever pitch over a bunch of horse shit they put out this weekend. Said we've already hauled in over four hundred suspects! Most already given polygraphs! Hell, if you've read the paper, you'd think the killers already turned themselves in. Sons of bitches are calling me asking for their names. Do me a favor. I know none of you have, but please don't talk with those idiot reporters till we get this thing solved."

"Don't let the bastards get to you, Barney," said Stanley. "They've been falling all over themselves for information. Best I figure, probably pulled it out of some mule's ass."

"I don't care whose ass they pulled it out of, Lieutenant; it's mine they're gonna hang if we don't hurry up and get this thing solved. These county folks are scared and mad as can be over these murders. We got a thousand houses up here, pump guns hanging out of every window. Folks are just spoiling to blow hell out of any damn thing that moves in the dark. We don't need any more killing. Anybody got anything else? No? All right, let's go to work."

From the start lawmen kept quiet about their suspects, but county folks didn't. Who-done-it murmurs became overnight rumors that within a few days had turned into downright accusations. "If there's any man in this county who could've done this, who'd do anything like this, it's Alex Evans, that's who." Alex was the buzz of Gwinnett, and he heard it from folks talking behind his back and soon to his face. There was no more "Howdy" or hat tipping. Only folks looking down their nose, whispering words of resentment. Cops got an earful too. "Y'all know good and well who done this. I seen him at Buford Diner this morning. When y'all gonna lock him up? Better yet, ya ought to hang him."

As county folks' suspicions grew, so too did Evans' paranoia. Soon after the murders, lawmen no longer had a need to go after Evans. He came to them. Believing he would still be deemed one in the brotherhood of law enforcement, Evans called on his former badge buddies for a display of alliance to his innocence.

Police Chief J. O. Bell's telephone rang late one evening. "Mr. Bell, sir, this is Alex Evans."

"Yeah, go ahead."

"Sir, I have a need in talking with you, but I'd like to do it face to face, if you don't mind."

"What's this about, Alex?"

"Well, sir, I'm a little nervous on this phone. Maybe, if you don't mind, I could come see you tonight, at your house."

"Yeah, that'll be fine, but you're coming alone. Don't bring nobody with you."

"No, sir, nobody but myself. Thank you, Chief. Be there in thirty minutes."

Bell hung up with Evans and immediately phoned GBI director, Major Barney Ragsdale. "Major, how are you? Chief Bell calling. I need a moment of your time."

"By all means, Chief, go ahead."

"Alex Evans just called me. Said he wants to come to my house, pay me a visit tonight. Said he needs to talk."

"What did you tell him, Chief?"

"Said, come on."

"Okay, good. Did he say what he wanted to talk about?"

"No. Seemed a might antsy though. Like something got his mind riled. Anything in particular you want me to talk about?"

"Chief, I don't know the man except to see him. You know him; you'll know what to talk about. And you can bet I'll be waiting to hear what you do. Call me whenever he leaves. That all right?"

"Be fine."

"Good to hear from you, J. O. Y'all doing okay?"

"Oh yeah, everyone's fine. Gonna stay that way too, with this .357 sitting here next to me."

Evans pulled into Chief Bell's front yard just before eight o'clock that evening. He got out of his car and walked up the steps of the front porch. Looking through the screen door, he announced, "Hello, Mr. Bell, it's me, Alex."

"Yeah, I can see you. Come on in."

Bell sat across the room in his overstuffed easy chair. A dimly lit reading lamp slanted over his shoulder. His arms rested atop the chair's broad sides. His bare feet lay crossed over a matching ottoman. The fingers of his left hand clenched a room-temperature can of Carling Black Label Beer. Four more sat atop the table next to him. In plain view his right hand securely gripped a loaded Smith and Wesson magnum revolver, finger inside the trigger guard. His cold gaze never broke from Evans. It was probably not the welcome Alex was hoping for.

J. O. swigged the last of his open beer. Popping another, he showed no intention of offering one to Evans.

Wide-eyed, Alex cleared his throat before starting. "I appreciate you seeing me on such short notice."

"Yeah, sure. Say, I ain't seen you round lately. Where you been?"

"Been around."

"Been where?"

"Oh, here and there, mostly away on business. Rest Haven, Dahlonega. North."

"You say?"

"Yes, sir."

"Alex, I don't recall you ever coming out here before. I'm just a little...some bit curious as why now. Said you wanna talk, sounded a might urgent. Something on your mind, is there?"

Evans nervously replied. "Well, yes, sir, there is. It's that I...well, it's just that I can't get over Jerry and Ralph and Mr. Gravitt, what was done to them. Those boys were close friends of mine. I can't figure out who on earth would do something like that to them. I saw Jerry and Ralph right before it happened. Came by my house. I figured I'd come out here to see...talk with you, see maybe who you think might've had anything to do with it."

Bell, not at all surprised with Evans verbal prod, said, "They're all working on it, Alex. I don't know anything yet. I don't think anybody does, just yet. Why?"

"Well, there're people who's talking. Maybe you've heard, people saying I had something to do with it, but I didn't."

"Is that what people are saying? You had something to do with it? Why would they say that, if you had nothing to do with it?"

"Chief, I swear to God, I had nothing to do with it, nothing whatsoever! I don't know why they're talking about me but, all I know is they are."

"Well, hell, Alex, let 'em talk, 'cause if you're saying you had nothing to do with it, then there ain't no need you worrying 'bout it, is there?"

"Mr. Bell, those officers were my best friends, so I was thinking, maybe I could be of some help. Maybe come up with a few names for you."

"Yeah, you do that, Alex." Bell took a gulp from his just-opened beer and stared at Evans while he swallowed. "Yeah, you do that all right."

"If you want, give me some leads, I'll snoop around for ya. Chief, I can go places and talk to people your boys can't. I'll be glad to do it; that is, if you want me to."

Bell became more agitated with Evans' assertion. "Alex, I don't think that'd be proper, with you being in the hot water you're already in. Besides, I told you, I don't know nothing except they're all working' on it. Ain't mine to say."

"Yes, sir. Just thought I'd ask. I'll still keep my ears open to whatever might come up and pass it on if it's something I think you oughta know. You and me, okay?"

Chief Bell straightened up firm in his chair. "Evans, I'm gonna tell you something, and best you listen real good what I'm fixing to say. I don't like you, boy. Don't like nothing 'bout you. I ain't gonna take too kindly to you coming back here. Don't telephone me neither. You hear what I'm saying? Am I making myself clear on that?"

"Yes, sir, Chief, I hear you clear. I know you're upset about what happened. Me too, but I don't know why you're feeling this way. I'm sorry you do. Guess I'll be leaving now."

After Evans left, Bell phoned Ragsdale. "He's come and gone."

"What'd he say?"

"Pretty much what I expected. I got more from him by the way he sat."

"How's that, J. O.?"

"Wouldn't look me in my face. Mostly looked at the floor, rubbing his hands real fidgety, nervous, like a cat-scared little bird."

☙

Evans staged his play for an alliance a half dozen more times, all the same: his phone call to lawmen asking to see them; their "Come on in" greeting from an easy chair, beer in one hand, revolver in the other; his prods for information and offers of help; their repeat of his questions; his unprovoked assertion of innocence. "It wasn't me; I couldn't have; I wouldn't have; they were my best friends." Their distrust before he visited, him appearing miffed by their resentment when leaving. Finally the "He's come and gone" phone call to Major Ragsdale, who logged every instance. "Let's just sit back and let ol' Alex incriminate himself. He don't need us; he's doing a damn fine job on his own."

While clueless that M. C. Perry had ratted him out, Evans could see that his old cop buddies weren't going to support his claim of innocence or rally to his defense if he was charged with the murders.

Held in a ring of suspicion with nowhere to hide, Evans did what he felt was most logical. He hid in the open. He went back to the very people he tried to run from. Evans staged a charade to convince anyone who'd listen that he was a morally upright, wholesome man absolutely innocent of murder or any other crime. Confident his ruse would work, he built an alibi as to why it couldn't have been him.

Building a defense without judicial cause can be a risky move; for Alex Evans, it was a costly mistake. "Everybody in this county is a suspect; I know I am," he told several people. Taking this a step further, to a point of extreme absurdity, he said, "I'll prove I had nothing to do with it. I'll solve this crime myself." He claimed that the grieving families had requested his service. "They've told me they want a real investigator working this case," Evans declared. "Those murdered officers were my very close friends. To bring justice for them and their families, I will use all my investigative abilities to find the killers on my own. I believe those murders involved people in this county who're above the law, people who can't be prosecuted and will never be brought to justice. Unlike law enforcement and our judicial system, I have no attachment to any of those people but to see that they're held responsible for what they've done. I will take it upon myself to investigate this crime, and if these murders aren't solved by the time I get out of federal prison serving time for an offense I did not commit, I will start right back where I left off and not stop until I've solved it."

Evans stitched a tale cut from whole cloth about Gwinnett corruption. "It originates from county commissioners and businessmen puppeteering the entire justice system. The courts, judges, sheriff, and police... they're all in on it. It's all tied to law enforcement and the mighty dollar. Cops, crooks, and thieves all in bed together. Two dozen of the county's 'finest' citizens, businessmen, and our elected officials are crime bosses of a criminal syndicate. I know it for a fact. They're the ones who did this. It was a conspiracy. Those policemen knew what I know and were fixing to blow the lid off this whole thing. That's why they were killed, to shut them up."

Evans gave names of who they were, what they were doing, and details of how this criminal enterprise worked. He duped an Atlanta television news reporter into joining along with his investigative sham. "We're gonna blow the lid off every criminal activity in this county. We're gonna root out those killers and you'll get credit for the dig. Me, I just wanna see justice for my friends."

Having no conscience but a boatload of gall, Alex Evans visited the murdered officers' homes. At each house, sitting mere feet from where the policeman's open casket had lain earlier, caskets he never saw, Evans promised the families: "I'm gonna solve this crime. I'm gonna bring the justice y'all deserve." To that end, he had the nerve to ask, "If you have any information that will help my investigation, please let me know."

The families were not amused, and they certainly took no comfort in knowing that the disgraced former deputy was "on the case."

After Evans' visit to the Everetts' house, Daddy Lee Everett said to his wife, "Investigator! That's a field of bull dirt! He's a liar! Only thing he ever done was run off shine boys. Hell, anyone can find 'em if you the law. Follow the sugar, that's all you gotta do. Everybody knows that. He ain't no damn investigator."

❧

Annoyed from the start, Ragsdale soon discovered Evans pulled his most outrageous stunt. Ragsdale called his lead investigator, Arthur Hutchins, and blurted, "Arthur, I just got an earful from Lowell Connor. Seems Alex Evans sent a telegram to President Johnson. Wants him to send the FBI in on our case! All this garbage he's been puking has got feathers ruffled under the gold dome. Governor's mansion too! Damn it, Art, I ain't gonna take any more of Connors' shit. It's time we had a little talk with Mr. Evans."

"Talk to him about what?"

"Oh hell, Art, not you too!"

"Major, we have nothing to arrest him on."

"I know that. Pull his ass in anyway! Tell him he's high on the list. Hell, tell him anything you want, just pull him in so we can shut that goddamn mouth of his, or we'll all be regretting it soon."

Hutchins telephoned Evans demanding he meet him at GBI headquarters in Atlanta. The building, Georgia's law enforcement command center, held the offices of the public safety commissioner, the state police as well as the Georgia Bureau of Investigation.

Ragsdale would join Hutchins for their meeting in the Gwinnett room, so named as synonymous with the murders. The room, a windowless storage area at the far end of the basement, had been converted to a central holding vault for all documents, files and reports relevant to the investigation. Taped to each side of its only door was a warning, handwritten on notebook paper. Do Not Remove Any Files from This Room! signed by Major Ragsdale.

Crammed inside the gray cinderblock walls stood two six-foot-long folding tables. Two metal chairs sat on either side. Another chair sat wedged between an old wooden desk and the back wall. Within arm's reach were two four-drawer filing cabinets flush against the far corner. On top of one cabinet was a report sign-in sheet. A placard hung above the other, April 17, 1964, meant as a hounding reminder to all of the date the case opened.

Evans arrived at the downtown headquarters building and was immediately escorted to the Gwinnett room where the two state agents waited to question him. He entered the room to see Hutchins sitting behind the desk. Ragsdale stood leaning against the file cabinets, and pointed with his finger. "Grab a chair and sit in front of this desk."

The other man said, "Alex, I'm Captain Arthur Hutchins. I'm assistant director of the GBI, and this is Director Major Barney Ragsdale."

"Yes, I know who you gentlemen are."

"Well good, that puts us on mutual ground because, and I mean this literally, Alex, we know who you are. Do you know why we called you down here?"

"I think I have an idea."

"Please don't play coy with us, Mr. Evans. I think you have more than just an idea as to why you're here. This will go much easier if you play straight up with your answers."

"Sure, Mr. Hutchins, of course."

"We've heard that you're investigating the triple murder of those Gwinnett County policemen. Is that so?"

"You could say I've looked into it. Those policemen, the three policemen that were murdered, were close friends of mine. I've visited with their families, and they asked me to look into it."

"No, Alex, I've heard you're doing more than just looking into it. A whole lot more. Seems as though you're conducting a full-fledged investigation on your own. Is that right?"

"Oh no, you've got me all wrong, Mr. Hutchins."

"Is that right?"

"Like I said, those officers were close friends of mine. I'm not doing anything that's against the law. At least in my opinion, as far as I know, I don't think I'm breaking any laws. Just doing as the families have asked. You know, a friend helping out friends is all."

Ragsdale asked, "By whose authority are you conducting 'your' investigation, Mr. Evans?"

"Since you put it that way, I guess nobody's."

Hutchins inquired, "Alex, did you send a wire to President Johnson?"

"Yes sir, well really, no sir. I helped Kelly Everett. He asked me to write the words, but he sent it. His signature was on it."

"Why?"

"I...me and Kelly, that is, were talking about it, and he thought President Johnson should know. Kelly felt, it being such a big deal and all, that he should authorize the FBI to help with the investigation."

"What has your investigation come up with, Mr. Evans? Keep in mind we are the law, and we're in charge."

"Yes sir, Mr. Ragsdale. It's a long story, but basically Gwinnett County is run by people I know are above the law. And I know about the workings of the county's crime syndicate much more than you all do. I can go places you and your people can't, because I'm not the law. Folks don't need to worry about me. You see, Mr. Hutchins, in Gwinnett, and I know that county inside out, this crime syndicate I referred to is naturally run by bosses, crime bosses. I know who they are. Those officers knew what I know. They were close to exposing not just the bosses but the entire syndicate. The men who hold all the power up there weren't going to let that happen, Mr. Ragsdale. As a result the three officers had to be silenced. That's why they were murdered. It was a conspiracy building for some time now. I have a pretty good feel for who could have done this crime, and in time I will have enough information to point fingers at the gunmen. Of course the men, the boss men of the syndicate, didn't actually pull the trigger, but they're the ones who had it done. Problem is it's going to be hard enough to prove even for someone like me who knows these people, let alone any law enforcement agency. Forget that. I don't care who you're with, because, gentlemen, let me assure you, these people are very mysterious in how they carry out their business. They can cover up their crimes to where there's no way you'll ever connect them to anything. They know how to keep one step ahead of you all, believe me. And I'll tell you another something. You've got more than a few who're in law enforcement that work for them. I'm not just talking about patrol cops, either. You got higher ups on the take, too. I know this for a fact. I wouldn't hold it past any of them to have been in on this, and that's unfortunate, because now we see how they deal with their own who don't play along with the game. Trust me, gentlemen, they get what they want, and they ain't finished."

Hutchins raised his eyebrows. "Alex, do you know anything about the nineteen sixty-three Oldsmobile found burned at the crime scene on Arc Road?"

"No, sir, sure don't."

"You weren't looking for a nineteen sixty-three Oldsmobile to steal, by any chance?"

"I have no idea what you're talking about, Mr. Ragsdale, sir. I don't steal cars, sir. I'm not a thief, sir."

Hutchins continued, "Where were you the night of the murders?"

"At home with my wife. I was on a business trip up north of Rest Haven that day and didn't get home until I think around nine o'clock that evening and never left my house after I got home. Not that night. Actually I never left my house until the next day...afternoon."

Ragsdale placed both his hands atop the desk. "Mr. Evans, during the early morning hours of April seventeenth, did you murder those three policemen on Arc Road?"

"I don't know any Arc Road. I've never been on that road in my life."

"My question was did you murder those three policemen?"

"You heard me, you know what I said."

"Remind me. Say it again."

"I was at home with my wife and kids. I can't be in two places at one time. I'm good, but not that good."

Evans' smirk sent Ragsdale into rage. "Mr. Evans, you are going to stop this hokey investigation of yours, whether you have anyone's blessings or not. You're going to stop it right now. No more accusations, no more television interviews, no more telegrams to the President, nothing. You got that? We're in charge of this investigation, and we don't need your or anyone else's interference."

"Yes, sir, I mean no, sir, I won't interfere, but I won't run and hide, either."

"What do you mean by that, Alex?" Hutchins asked.

"It just so happens I'm right in the middle of this thing. If me or my family is threatened by these people, I'll have no choice but to do what I have to do. What I'm saying is if it's the people I'm thinking it is, then I won't hesitate to defend myself and my family against who I believe is responsible for killing my friends."

Ragsdale pursed his lips and thought for a moment. "Mr. Evans, I'm curious. You say those officers were murdered—silenced is how you put it—because they knew about this so-called crime syndicate and were going to expose it, is that right?"

"That's right."

"If you're claiming you know what the three police officers knew, why hasn't this crime syndicate put a hit on you? After all, if they're bold enough to murder three police officers, what would keep them from killing off someone like you?"

"I guess you're just gonna have to find that out for yourself, aren't you?"

Ragsdale's patience snapped, "There is no crime syndicate run by crime bosses, Mr. Evans. There was no conspiracy to silence anybody. This is all a load of fiction that's come from your imagination."

"No, sir, it's not, and I can prove it."

"You can prove nothing," Ragsdale countered.

Evans shrugged. "Oh yes, I can, and if you'll let me, I will."

"Let me tell you something," said Ragsdale. "And I know this for a fact. We have more leads than you might think. We know there were three killers there that night. We have the names of two, and soon we'll have the third. It won't be long before we make an arrest, and when we do, we're going to see they have their day in court. We're going to find them guilty, and in short order, we're going to strap them in that electric chair at Reidsville, and then we're gonna light them up."

Evans strained twice to swallow. "Yeah, I'm sure of that."

Hutchins took over. "You may leave for now, Alex, but we'll stay in touch, all right?"

Evans stood while struggling to maintain an innocent man's composure. "Sure."

Immediately after Evans left, the two agents talked. Barney Ragsdale showed a rare face of frustration, "Arthur, in all my years of interrogating creeps, I've never come across anyone as arrogant or with as big an ego as that S.O.B. He's guilty as sin. We've just got to prove it."

"I wish us luck on that," said Hutchins.

❧

The case took a turn that August. On a hunch leading from word of an Oldsmobile wreck four months earlier, John Crunkleton sifted through accident files inside the

Lawrenceville City Police Department. Buried deep inside a cabinet Crunkleton found one report that finally gave Captain Hutchins the missing link he'd been looking for. It would prove to be their biggest break yet in the investigation. The report detailed an incident that occurred not less than a quarter mile from their City Hall meeting the previous April. Four weeks prior to the murders, a city fire truck sideswiped a maroon 1963 two-door Oldsmobile Super 88 in the Main Street intersection of downtown Lawrenceville. The fire truck received minor front-bumper damage, but the Olds took a solid punch to its left side, bending the frame, wheels, and rear bumper. The driver's door, rear quarter panel, and trunk lid were crumpled, the roof warped, and the windshield broken.

Hutchins tracked the Oldsmobile to its original owner, who told him the car had been written off as a total loss by the Maryland Casualty Insurance Company. The insurance company's records showed that Auto Salvage Wrecker Service towed the car from the crash site to White's Body Shop on March 19. White's held the car in storage for Maryland Casualty until it was sold as salvage.

Hutchins drove to the body shop, where he asked to talk to the owner, but found the owner's son, Paul Meier, instead. Paul, cleaning shop tools in the garage, struck Hutchins as an honest young man with amiable qualities, cool and friendly.

Hutchins asked, "Paul, did you have a nineteen sixty-three Oldsmobile in your possession around March of this year?"

"Yep, did."

"Could you describe that car as best you remember?"

"Like you said, a sixty-three Olds. Was a maroon Super eighty-eight, two-door hardtop, as I recall."

"What kind of shape was it in when you got it?"

"Left side was all tore up. Shame seeing a new car like that."

"Fixable?"

"Hardly!"

"Do you still have the car here?"

"Nope, sold it."

"When? You remember?"

"Let's see here." He flipped through his paperwork for the months of March and April. "Yep, here it is. Sold it on the second day of April. Got two checks, one-thousand one-hundred sixty eight dollars for the car, sixty-eight dollars for the storage."

"Does your paperwork show who bought it?"

"Yep, sure does. Leroy Thomas."

Hutchins slumped. "Who is Leroy Thomas? Do you know him? What was he going to do with the car?"

"I don't know him, but I know the car wasn't for him; he just wrote the checks. He was financing the deal for this other fella."

"Do you know who the other man is? His name?"

"Yep, well, don't really know him, only seen him out a time or two. Name is Venson Williams. That's who really bought the car. Mr. Thomas just paid for it is how I understood."

When Hutchins heard the name, he froze. His eyes stare fixed on the boy's face. As he surmised four months earlier, this link was too coincidental not to be part of a motive.

The smiling young man stared at the motionless Hutchins, "Mister, you all right? You look like you just seen a ghost."

"Paul, did Leroy Thomas take the car when he paid for it?"

"Nope, Venson Williams came out here two, three days later and got it."

"How did he get it?"

"Fella by the name of Dave Dickson's got a wrecker service. Him and Williams come out here together and towed it off."

"Do you know where they took it?"

"Nope, I have no idea. I got Mr. Dickson's number here, if you want it. I'm sure he can tell you."

"All right, Paul, you've been a big help. Do yourself a favor and keep quiet about this."

∽

With two state troopers riding along, Hutchins drove to the wrecker yard unannounced, hoping to catch Dickson off guard. On the way his mind speculated. Was Dickson with Williams the night of the murders? Could he be the third man whose shoeprints were found in the Arc Road dirt? Would this new information lead Hutchins to crack the biggest murder case ever in the state of Georgia?

With a momentum of good luck finally on his side, Hutchins pulled into the wrecker yard and spotted a man sitting behind the office counter.

"Sir, I'm Arthur Hutchins with the GBI. You Dave Dickson?"

Dickson looked exactly like what Hutchins expected for a tow truck driver. He had a big upper body, blacksmith arms, and a gritty manner. "Yeah, I'm Dickson. What can I do for you?"

"You heard about the three Gwinnett County policemen murdered back in April?"

"Damn sure did! I reckon there ain't nobody who hadn't. Listen, was they really handcuffed, all three together?"

In no mood to field questions from a suspect, Hutchins stood on guard facing the man he must consider, at this point, a cop killer. "Where were you the night of April sixteenth, morning of the seventeenth?"

"New York City, visiting with kin. Why in the hell they'd ever want to live up there I don't know. Stinking Yankees. Anyways, that's when I heard, or should say read it on the front page of the newspaper."

Hutchins settled. "Do you know anything about the car found burned at the crime scene?"

"What car?"

"The torched car. Know anything about it?"

"Nope. Well, wait a minute. Believe I read it was an Olds, wasn't it? Why do you ask?"

"According to White's Body Shop, you towed a car out of their yard the first week in April. Is that so?"

"Did, yes, sir. Sixty-three, I believe, two-door Olds Super eighty-eight, maroon, dark-red whatever. Why?"

"Did someone hire you for that tow job?"

"Yeah, fella by the name of Venson Williams."

"How do you know this fella, Venson Williams?"

"Don't much, just around. Something he done?"

"Did he ride with you when you towed the car from White's?"

Dickson nodded. "Yeah, rode with me, sure did."

"Did anybody else ride with you other than Venson?"

"No. Why all the questions?"

"Where did you and Venson take the car?"

"Hartsville, South Carolina. Something happen?"

"All the way to South Carolina?"

"Well, seeing how you're asking, I'll be right honest with you, Mr. Hutchins, I couldn't find no reason for hauling it all the way out there if he's only gonna cut it up for parts, but I figured, so be it. I get paid by the mile.

Time I get my money, it don't matter to me what he does with that car. Stick it up his ass, for all I care."

"That's what he told you? Going to cut it up for parts?"

"No, as a matter of fact said he was gonna fix the car for his self. I thought he was just kidding me, 'cause, see, that car wasn't no fixer. Was tore all to hell. Parts was all it's worth. But damn if Venson didn't tell me he was gonna fix it for his self. Said he knew where to get a good deal on what was needed."

"Did you go straight to Hartsville that day?"

Dickson nods. "Straight to Hartsville. Got him a shop. Him and his partner, on the side of a little gas station. Why?"

Hutchins raised his eyebrows, "Partner? Did he mention his partner's name?"

"Yeah, was there whenever we pulled in. Wade Truett, I believe."

"Tell me that name again?"

"Wade Truett is how I heard it. Was waiting on us whenever we got there. Said he's a body and wrench man, could do wonders fixing up cars. I told Venson it was gonna take more than wonders fixing that car. More like a goddamn miracle!"

"Describe this man for me, his partner."

"Wiry, late twenties, early thirties, maybe. Six foot, little more. One hundred sixty or seventy pounds. Didn't pay a whole lotta attention to him. All I wanted to do was let the car down, pull the hooks, and get on back. Driving at dark ain't my cup of tea."

"The car you towed to Hartsville…"

"Yeah, nice car, Super eighty-eight."

"The one you towed to Hartsville for Williams?"

"Mr. Hutchins, I've been in this business, wrecked-car business, coming on thirty years. Made a good living on wrecked cars. Don't take me but quick to size one up to the dollar. Rebuilt more than a few, but cut most down for parts. I know how much those parts sell for, and I know the time it takes to rebuild a wrecked car, if you do it right. That car of Williams, even if he was to get free parts, time it'd take to fix it, ain't no money to be made. That car would cost you money. The frame was bent! Ain't gonna make no money on that car. If that's the way he's gonna do his business, he ain't gonna be doing it long."

"Do you know where he could get free parts to fix the car?"

"Not here!"

"I'll be back in touch. Thank you for your time today."

"Say, look here, Mr. Hutchins, am I in some kind of trouble? Do I need to worry 'bout any of this?"

"I don't know" the lawman stared into the man's eyes. "Do you?"

"No, sir, I don't guess I do."

"No, Mr. Dickson, you don't. You're fine. No trouble."

Hutchins decided he knew the motive for stealing Arc Road's sixty-three Olds, and of the two names he had, one was confirmed to go with it, Venson Williams. Did he have his third man in either of Williams' partners, Leroy Thomas or Wade Truett?

Using the element of surprise, that evening Hutchins and two state patrolmen knocked unannounced on Leroy Thomas' front door. Thomas and his wife cordially invited the men into their living room, but the warm welcome quickly cooled from the trooper's rigid posture. Hutchins hard-balled his first few questions, but as the interview proceeded, he realized Thomas was not his third man and softened his tone. He excused the patrolmen back outside to their car, and for thirty minutes Thomas answered what the agent asked.

Thomas admitted he knew Williams. "I've known him going on about three years now. We've done some car business together, fixing and selling. I bought a wrecked sixty-three Olds from White's Salvage yard on April second. Actually I financed the car for Venson."

Hutchins asked, "Financed it? Why?"

"Two reasons, to help Venson and to make a hundred dollars interest on the loan from profit he'd make selling the car after fixing it."

"How bad was the car wrecked?"

"I don't remember exactly. I just saw it the one time at White's. Venson knew all about it, I don't much get involved with the fixing part. That's his doings."

When Hutchins asked if Thomas had heard about the police murders, Thomas answered, "Yes, of course. Unbelievable!"

"Where were you on the night of April sixteenth?"

"I was here at home with my family and friends till late, maybe twelve thirty, one o'clock."

Thomas' alibi was verifiable. The time frame was well after the Olds was stolen.

"When's the last time you saw Venson?"

"I haven't seen him since then, last April. I've talked with him on the phone two or three times about how he's coming along on the car. I got nearly twelve hundred dollars tied up in that thing. Tell you the truth, I'm a little pissed off about that deal. Venson told me he'd have the car finished in six to eight weeks, and here we are six months later, and he still ain't got it done. Says he's had a hard time finding parts."

"Do you recall exactly when in April, the day it was, you last saw him?"

"Was the night of them murders you're talking about. Venson left his lighter on the table next to where he was sitting. I knew it must be his 'cause I seen where he'd scratched his initials on it. Figured I'd leave it right there so he'd see it next time he came by. Had it in my hand when I heard the radio tell about the murders. I'll always remember having Venson's lighter in my hand at that moment, and I remember it was the night before, when he left it."

"Would you mind if I held on to it for a while? I'll make sure you get it back, but just for a time, I'd like to have it."

"Not at all. Matter of fact, you can just keep it."

"What time was it when he came by that night, and how long did he stay, you remember?"

"Probably was about five thirty, somewhere along in there. We had some friends and a neighbor over, he didn't stay long. Thirty minutes, I figure."

"Why did he come by?"

"Venson usually drops by to say hello whenever he's coming through this way. No particular reason but to say hello is all."

"Did you see the car he was driving?"

"Yes, it was a sixty one, maybe sixty-two Chevy Impala convertible. Super Sport I believe, white with a white top."

"Mr. Thomas, was anybody with Venson when he came by that night, April sixteen?"

"Came with this fella lives over in South Carolina, Wade Truett. They's partners."

Although this was what the lawman wanted and needed to hear, he was still taken by surprise when he heard it. Showing no outward emotion, he reveled within. "That's it! This guy has put the finger on Williams and Truett together, here in Gwinnett, the night of the murders."

With what he learned from Dickson, and now Thomas, Hutchins felt certain. "There's no more maybe about it. Truett is my third man."

∽

Thirty-three-year-old South Carolina native Wade Levi Truett began his lifelong criminal career at a very young age. He would even admit, "I've been stealing something or another since the time I knew how to walk." By the time he was sixteen the law had tagged him a habitual repeat offender.

When Truett was eighteen a highly annoyed judge told him, "Mr. Truett, I've seen you in my courtroom one too many times." He offered Wade one of two choices, jail or Uncle Sam. Truett chose khakis over stripes, but the judge's hope for Truett going straight quickly slid away when within a year of Truett's enlistment, Washington State authorities arrested and convicted him in civilian court for burglarizing a convenience store. The Army declared him a soldier undesirable for duty and sent him packing back to Carolina with a dishonorable discharge. Home again, he worked as an auto mechanic, longshoreman, and truck driver part time, but thieving was his chosen full-time trade. Truett often said getting caught was simply a part of the trade. "And I pulled time on the chain gang more times than I care to remember." Married with six children, by the early 1960s Truett had no intention of giving up his full-time profession. He expanded his con to include auto theft, conspiracy, forgery, and larceny, which of course also expanded his criminal resume and lengthy arrest record.

In January 1964, Truett and Venson Williams formed a partnership operating a fixer-upper car business in Hartsville, South Carolina, Truett's hometown. As for their repair shop, Truett rented a one-car stall attached to his cousin's service station near Prestwood Lake.

Initially they drove up north, mostly Baltimore and New York, buying rusted-out winter cars to repair and resell, but the nickel-and-dime venture barely paid the rent. After not a whole lot of thought they came up with a new three-part business plan sure to make them "big money." One: buy late-model wrecked cars written off as a total loss by the insurance company. More costly to repair than they were worth, these cars were sold with a salvaged title legitimate for resale but normally the cars were sold as parts by the buyer. Two: find clean like-kind cars they could use for parts to repair the wrecked cars. And three: after finding the like-kind cars, steal them, strip them of all parts, fix their legit salvaged cars, and sell off the parts they didn't need. Left with only the frames, they'd cut them into small pieces and sell them to a scrapyard. In the end they would have a clean titled car with no trace possible to the stolen parts car. A torch; a few tools; a private, hidden garage; and a little know-how, all things they already had, and in their way of thinking, it was a new business plan for a surefire way of making big money.

On the night of the murders, Venson Williams and Wade Truett were free on bond while awaiting an appeal hearing for a federal conviction of conspiring to hijack an interstate tractor-trailer loaded with bonded red liquor, a crime they had both been convicted of one year earlier.

Hutchins left the Thomas house, got in the State Patrol car, and told his men, "First thing in the morning, boys, don't tell anybody, but we're going across the state line. We've got two car thieves turned cop killers I want to talk to. Gonna give the little bastards the scare of their lives. Pack your wheels with magnums, just in case."

The following morning, with the address he copied from Dickson's tow receipt, Hutchins and three uniformed Georgia state troopers met with a South Carolina agent and three of his troopers. From the local Waffle House they drove a short half mile before pulling into the front parking lot of the one-bay garage. With guns drawn the lawmen got out of their cars and surrounded the shop entrance. Even before Hutchins left his vehicle, he saw the wrecked Oldsmobile with Williams and Truett standing motionless at either end of the car.

As he exited his car, Hutchins hollered at the two men, "Boys, take your hands out of your pockets where I can see 'em."

Hutchins walked up to the front of the Olds where Truett was standing. He spoke loudly in a calm but commanding tone, "I'm Captain Arthur Hutchins with the Georgia Bureau of Investigation. Venson, come out from back there and stand here next to Wade."

Williams, acting nervous, looked scared but voiced anger. "What's this all about? Who the hell do you think you are coming in here with these troopers and guns?"

Hutchins, without taking his eyes off the two men, ordered the troopers, "You officers pat these boys down for weapons, please."

The two men looked startled by the sudden appearance of the lawmen and the GBI man who knew their names.

"They're clean," said the officers as they backed away.

Hutchins took out his cigarettes. "Give you boys a smoke?"

Both took one. Williams put the cigarette to his lips.

"Oh, here, Venson, let me light that for you." Hutchins held up the lighter he got from Leroy Thomas. He placed it in front of Williams' face close enough that Venson could clearly see his initials scribed in its side. His eyes expressed shock.

Hutchins flipped the top open with his thumb and then spun the flint wheel, flaming the wick. He lit the two cigarettes, snapped the top shut, reopened it, and spun the flint wheel, flaming the wick again while looking at the lighter. "You know something? I really like these big Zippos. Carried one through the Ardennes all the way to Berlin." Again he flipped the top open and closed. "Yes, sir, nothing like these big ones. Let me think now. Where did...you know, I can't remember where I got this one." He stared closer at the lighter. "Hm, I haven't noticed this before. Looks like someone carved their initials on this thing. Look here." He turned the lighter and showed it to Williams. "Yeah, here, you see it? Right here, V.E.W. Hey! Aren't those your initials, Venson? Well, I'll just be damned; those are your initials, aren't they? Venson Eugene Williams. How 'bout that?"

Hutchins folded the top closed and slid it back into his front pant pocket. "Wade, tell me about that nineteen sixty-three two-door maroon Oldsmobile."

"Yes, sir, well, ain't nothing much to tell about this car. We bought it from White's Body Shop in Atlanta. You want to see the bill of sale?"

"No, no, Wade, not this car, I know all about this car. I want to know about that sixty-three Oldsmobile you and Venson stole back in April, the sixteenth to be exact."

"Mr. Hutchins, I have no earthly idea what you're talking about. We didn't steal no car in...when did you say...April, was it? Listen, sir, we're just a small one-car shop here. Why would we steal a sixty-three Olds when we already got our hands full with this one? We got all the paperwork to show on this car. Even got parts receipts. Looks to me like you come all the way out here from Georgia for nothing."

"Don't think so, Wade." Hutchins took in a deep breath, shook his head, and then repeated his answer as he exhaled. "No, don't think so. You and Venson stole a car just like this one; same color, make, and model. You stole it out of a parking lot in an apartment complex near Lavista and Briarcliff Roads, not far off the I-85 expressway in Atlanta."

"You're full of horse shit, mister! You don't know what the hell you're talking about. And you can't prove a word of it, neither. We didn't steal no car. Didn't do no such a thing."

"Oh, is that right, Mr. Williams? Well, let me take you back to Thursday night, April the sixteenth. See if you might recall. Was sometime around eleven o'clock or so, the two of you and another man, who we already know, stole a nineteen sixty-three maroon two-door Oldsmobile hardtop in Atlanta. Drove it up the Northeast Expressway for about fourteen miles to Gwinnett County. Turned east on Beaver Ruin Road for just over a mile till you got to this little dirt road down there on the left. Road named Arc. Folks there saw you. An hour later, you set that Oldsmobile on fire, burned it to the ground. Don't you boys remember? Doesn't any of this ring a bell?"

Truett snorted out a half laugh. "Venson, I don't remember any of this. Do you?"

Williams threw his cigarette on the ground toward Hutchins' feet. "Hell no! He's full of shit. He can't prove none of it."

Hutchins stepped closer, staring into their faces, mere inches away. He stood straight. His eyes pierced into theirs. "Venson, see if I can't help your partner out here. Maybe this might jog his memory. At some point in time, after stealing that car then burning it down on that dirt road, somewhere there in between, the two of you handcuffed three Gwinnett County police officers, marched them into the woods, and murdered them. And with their own guns, you boys shot each one of those officers at close range multiple times in the head." The lawman nodded. "You're right, Venson, I can't prove it... least not yet I can't. But the two of you killed those police officers. I know you did, and you know you did. Just a matter of time, sooner more likely than later, I'll be back here to arrest you."

Before leaving, Hutchins asked Truett for the parts receipt. He made a few notes and then handed the receipt back. Hutchins sneered a menacing smile. "I'll be seeing y'all again real soon, you hear?" Stepping toward his car to leave, he gazed down. "Boys, pick up your cigarette butts you've thrown here on the ground or else these troopers will cite you for littering."

The lawmen returned to their car for the trip home to Georgia. Hutchins spotted the lawmen's surprised faces and pulled them together in a tight circle. He quietly told them, "All right, I can see what you're thinking, so listen up. You all don't know anything about what I discussed with those two. Do not talk to anyone concerning our trip out here today. Keep this between ourselves. They'll get their trial, fair and square. Nobody's going to deprive them of that. And they'll get their conviction too; nobody's going to deprive those officers' families of that. No, sir, we'll get our justice through a court of law and nowhere else. We're going to play this one by the book and leave matters to the Constitution, not to our emotions." The longtime GBI agent paused, making sure the troopers were listening. "You know, men, I'd personally like to rip the smirk off that little weasel Truett's face, but neither I nor you can, and if anybody else so much as tries, I'll hold every one of you responsible. Understand? I think you know what I'm talking about, but just so there's no confusion on your part, I have zero tolerance for vigilante justice, not from you or any of our people, understand? Zero!"

Obviously angered by what Truett and especially Williams had said, the men paused, nodded, and then quietly mumbled, "Yes, sir."

"I hope so, fellas. You don't want to be on my bad side."

Without placing a hard demand for secrecy, Hutchins believed every cop in Georgia and South Carolina would've soon taken up sniper positions around the little garage. Lawman's justice would've come swiftly. Truett and Williams would've never had a chance for a trial, and Hutchins knew the whole county of Gwinnett would've been denied its justice.

࿇

Neither Williams nor Truett had spoken a single word to each other about that horrific night the previous April. Six months later, they stood stunned as they watched lawmen drive away.

Venson spit on the ground. "Shit! I knew this was gonna happen. We're in it now, boy. Damn it, if it hadn't been for that dirty son of a bitch Evans shooting that cop we wouldn't be in this mess."

Truett shook his head. "Only dirty son of a bitch I saw shooting any cop was you, buddy! Why'd you do it? Why'd you have to kill 'em? I never said we ought to shoot 'em! That's all on you! You and that crazy-ass Alex! Venson, I'm telling you right now, I ain't taking no murder rap for killing them polices. No siree, buddy, not me!"

"Shut your mouth! We're both deep in this shit now, you same as me. Listen, Wade, that Georgia bastard ain't just kidding, they'll strap us in that chair!"

"Oh no, buddy! Bullshit to that! What the hell you saying 'us' for?"

"Us as in us! You and me, sweetheart; that's what for. Oh shit, son, you ain't got a clue in that stupid-ass brain of yours, do you? Let me think. Hell, they ain't got nothing on us, not one damn thing."

"Oh yeah? Is that right? Well, they got your lighter, don't they? How'd they get that?"

"How the hell do I know how he got it? I must've dropped it on that dirt road, maybe when I was getting in and out of them cars or maybe, buddy, when I was crawling around digging your dumb ass out of the dirt where you got the Chevy stuck. You remember that? Oh yeah, that's right. You, the one driving the getaway car! You may think you ain't taking no rap, but you ain't got no choice now. You're in it all the way up to your pretty little neck. Bet your sweet ass! And why the hell did you give him the parts receipt? What were you thinking? Wade, you got a big family with lots of kids. Better keep your mouth shut unless you don't care if they never see their daddy no more."

"Yeah? We'll see about that. Let me remind you of something. I didn't kill them cops, Venson, and I ain't taking no blame for it. You can tell your buddy Alex that too. Tell him I said I ain't taking no blame for what you and him did. He's your friend, not mine. I don't care, 'cause right now, I don't give a rat's ass for nothing anymore; not this car, not you, not Alex. Nothing! Get this thing out of my shop! Take it to your buddy Leroy, just like it is. That's fine with me. I'm finished. Take your tools too. I'm done with you and this whole damn mess. You already got me in this shit-deep enough. If you think you're gonna drag me in it any further, you got another think coming. I'll call that lawman back so fast it'll make your head spin. I'll tell him everything. I mean it. Think I'm not serious? Try me! Now get your damn shit out of here and leave me and my family out of this, or else."

Their new business plan for making big money, supposedly surefire, flamed out, plus they lost their appeal on the liquor conviction. Eight weeks after breaking their partnership, each began a two-year Fed stretch for hijacking the trailer-load of bonded Kentucky whiskey. Truett went to the Federal Corrections Institute in Tallahassee, Florida; Williams resided inside the Atlanta Federal Penitentiary.

All the while, as Captain Hutchins worked his side; DeKalb county detectives John Crunkleton and Homer Lee Cheek worked Gwinnett. They did exactly what they'd said, "Somebody besides M. C. Perry knows something. We're gonna turn this county upside down till we find out who."

For six tedious months, the detectives shook down every Gwinnett grease monkey who'd ever lit a torch or turned a wrench, their daddies and uncles too. They investigated every backyard engine swap and what tree branch the pulling chain hung from. They gave no favor to reputation no matter how deep-rooted or stellar. If a man owned or worked at a gas station, service garage, or parts house, he got the third degree. They scoured every piece of car-related inventory in the county until every part had been accounted for. A business owner found himself in deep if so much as one can of motor oil was on his shelf that didn't match an invoice on his books. They sifted through every group in Gwinnett, showing no favoritism, and nobody, not even the law, escaped their dragnet. By the time their investigation was complete, they'd done as promised; they turned the county over, up one side, down the other, inside out. What the two detectives found was Barney Ragsdale had it pegged all along when he told Evans there was no crime syndicate run by crime bosses. There was no conspiracy to silence anybody.

In late autumn of 1964 the investigation stalled. Aside from those few but important leads at the beginning and those found by Hutchins since, all other suspects were either cleared or dismissed. No credible leads remained for examination. Several fame seekers crawled out of their holes claiming knowledge of the crime for sheer notoriety. Reporters quickly converged, first to indulge their fantasies and then to exploit the story. Front page splatter followed with bold headlines reading Breaking News in the Police Murders. But typically there was no news, breaking or otherwise.

At the April meeting in Lawrenceville, Ragsdale had warned investigators to steer clear of reporters, and they did. Often lawmen would pay respectful visits to each officer's family, but even then they shared no information regarding suspects. From time to time side stories grabbed a column in the editorials: Governor Declares Day of Memorial for Slain Officers, Widow's Fund Falls Short of Expectations, just enough chatter to keep Georgia's number-one news story alive and copies selling.

It was the constant media badger of No Leads in Gruesome Cop Slayings and voter unrest from what appeared to be an ineffective effort of solving the crime, however, that finally capped the governor and safety commissioner's ire.

Commissioner Lowell Conner commanded Barney Ragsdale to affect change. "Major, get someone who can put this investigation back on track and solve it. I don't care who you put in charge. Get it solved!"

In early November, Barney Ragsdale called Captain Hutchins to his office. "Art, I know it's been a long road for you in this investigation. You've done your usual fine job."

Hutchins, having heard the murmurs himself, said, "Barney, sounds to me like there's a swan-song coming."

"You gotta know it, just hear me out, will you? Connor and the gold-dome boys believe we've gone as far as we can with the current lineup. I agree with 'em. We need a fresh approach. Robert Hightower is coming in to take the lead, but he doesn't know it. He'll be coming through Atlanta tomorrow and I've asked him to drop by for coffee. I'm gonna surprise him with the news."

"I agree with you, Major. We've got a hold on the culprits, but not on the case. Frankly, I'm stumped on how to seal this thing. Bob can look at it from, as you say, a fresh angle. You also say you're going to surprise Hightower? Well, I know better. He's a good man, and a fine investigator. But he's not the surprisable type. He'll take it in his usual stride. I just hope he doesn't care much for sleep. He's sure as hell not going to get any."

⁊

Robert Hightower had completed his military service as a distinguished member of the elite Navy Underwater Demolition Team and went on to graduate from the FBI National Academy in Washington, D.C. After serving one year with the FBI, he spent seven years with the Metropolitan Washington D.C. Police Department as a detective in the special crimes unit. Returning to his southern roots he accepted an offer from the GBI as its chief instructor for major case studies at the Georgia Police Academy in Milledgeville, established just two years before the murders. A self-motivated man, Hightower had an enforcement philosophy that was by-the-book protocol with a unique twist, a talent at seeing evidence from a different point of view, finding direction in what seemed to be a lost cause and concluding with a conviction by a jury in the court of law. Although greatly admired and respected for his achievements, he was a humble man.

∾

Hightower arrived the following afternoon and waited in the lobby of the GBI headquarters.

Ragsdale walked into the lobby. "Bob, thanks for coming by. How was your drive here?"

"Went well, Major. Thanks. Good to see you."

"Let me get you a cup of coffee, but first, I'd like to show you something."

"Sure. My time is yours."

Ragsdale took Hightower to the Gwinnett room, opened the door, and flipped on the light switch. Both men walked inside. "Here we are, what do you think about this setup?"

Hightower chuckled. "Major, am I supposed to say something complimentary or give you my honest opinion?"

"You've heard about the three police officers murdered up in Gwinnett County last April, right?"

"Of course. Captain Hutchins has lead on that. How's it coming?"

"He doesn't, and it isn't!"

"How's that?"

"I've relieved Arthur as lead. He's taken it down the road, identified suspects, motive, witnesses, and timeline, but still we're not anywhere close to going to the grand jury for indictments. This has been a frustrating case, especially with Lowell Connor and the governor snapping at my ass. Let me spell it out for you. My back and that of this whole agency is against the wall. These murders are the biggest story ever to come out of this state, and here we are seven months later with nothing but a bunch of politicians and reporters banging on our door."

Hightower mused, "So what's your plan?"

"Oh, I think you've probably figured it out by now. But in case you haven't, I didn't call you here just to meet the guys. You're here because I've appointed you as lead investigator on this case. This room will be your new office."

Ragsdale pointed at the two file cabinets against the back wall. "Arthur and I are confident that in those file drawers there's enough information to draw a path straight to the grand jury, and we're counting on you to do it. I'll give you every resource we've got, and if you need more, all you have to do is ask and it's yours."

Hightower raised his eyebrows and looked around the tiny room. "Office, huh? Major, if you hadn't told me, I would've sworn it was a dungeon."

Ragsdale smiled, "Well, we wanted you to feel at home. So glad you like it."

Hightower closed the door behind Ragsdale from inside his new office to begin what would become a full year of painstaking diligence. Completely unfamiliar with the investigation, he first pulled every folder from the crammed file cabinets and spread them across the two six-foot-long folding tables. The files were a poorly organized mess. Some reports were merely notes scribbled on a torn piece of paper or a name with phone number on the back of a matchbook cover.

For nearly two months secluded inside the windowless room, ignorant of night or day, every day of each week, and leaving only to sleep and shower in his hotel room, Hightower devoured the reports page for page, word for word. From organizing the scattered stretch of folders, he became an expert on the crime. He discovered that many areas of the investigation fell short of completion, leaving critical questions unanswered, which was perfect for Robert Hightower. His talent was identifying an investigation's weakness and then finding clarity in the muddle.

In late December, Hightower finished his review of the investigation and placed most, but not all, pieces of the puzzle together. He called Ragsdale and Hutchins to join him in the Gwinnett room.

The two boss-level agents entered Hightower's office. Ragsdale looked at Hutchins in astonishment. He looked at Hightower. "Beautiful! Bob, I could use a little of this charm in my office." Hightower had commandeered several light fixtures. One was a floor-standing carved mahogany job he had lifted on a late sleepless night from the director's very own office. Still perturbed over its disappearance, Ragsdale asked Hightower, "Hey! Where did you get that?" Hightower queried the director, "Didn't you tell me 'every resource'? Ain't it nice?"

"Gentlemen, please." Hightower waved them Matador style to matching upholstered high-back chairs recently seized from the bureau's entrance lobby. "First let me say you have indeed put together enough information to work with. From what I've discovered, you're on the right track, but there're some holes that need plugging.

If I can plug those holes, we've got a strong case. Let me explain."

Hightower gently, almost passionately, straightened the few file folders positioned only slightly crooked among many that stretched neatly across the two six-foot tables. "Captain, I agree with your findings as to suspects. The witnesses you've interviewed fit a timeline of events for motive. The murders were an unfortunate end result of the primary crime, auto theft, which plays into 'during a conspiracy,' which places them in a conscious mind for first degree murder, premeditated. I don't see a need to discuss these reports but rather my intentions moving forward on those charges. However, the only chance of that happening is either by finding a solid eyewitness or some piece of irrefutable evidence that puts the suspects at the crime scene. Better yet, both."

Hutchins said, "That's what we've been digging for, but there's no such person or evidence we've found."

Hightower noted, "I don't see any report on the license plate from the stolen Oldsmobile. Did it ever turn up? Same with the keys to the patrol car. Ever find those?"

Hutchins shook his head. "Nothing on the plate or keys. The only evidence from the crime scene belonged to the three officers and the burned Olds. There's no suspect linked to any evidence and we don't have any eyewitnesses."

"Actually, Captain, there is. There is evidence: the plate and keys. They're probably still somewhere at the crime scene. The thieves wouldn't have driven that stolen car from Atlanta to Gwinnett without a tag on it; too risky. Yet from what I see of the crime scene photos, there's no tag. Somebody took it off, and that somebody knows where it is. And we do have eyewitnesses as well. Four to be exact; the resident on Arc Road, who may be a little uncertain about what he saw, but still he saw something. Hightower spread three mugshot photos from his picture collection. And there's the three suspects: Evans, Truett, and Williams."

"The old man on Arc won't be much help," said Hutchins. Pointing at the pictures, he continued, "And if you're thinking about a confession from these three, I can tell you Evans is a hard-core pathological liar, extremely delusional. Believes every word he says. He's been doing what he calls his own investigation. It's nothing more than smoke and mirrors, a diversion from guilt through publicity. A man with no culpability has no need for taking action. You'll get no confession from him."

Hutchins continued his opinion based on the visit he made to Hartsville. Thumping the middle picture, "Williams? I have no doubt about his involvement. He's a definite player. But he's scared, running from the truth or someone or both. He displays defensive hostility to cover it up, but it's a fear like I've never seen in a man's face, one that'll prevent him from ever talking, I believe."

The former lead agent circled the folding tables. He tilted his head back and rubbed under his chin. His slowly spoken musings supported Hightower's theory. "Now, our boy Truett here is the youngest of the bunch. Calm, well collected, as if he's innocent, but I don't think so. He comes across with nonchalance as if he's oblivious to my allegations. The expression on his face didn't match the words from his mouth, though. Of the three, you may be able to find a crack in his armor but these other two, no, not them."

"That may be the case, but when a man's life is at stake he can get real talkative. Captain, I think you're right about Evans and Williams, Truett too. The one who shows the most calm is usually the one who has the softest skin. He'll be the first to crack." Hightower tapped on the mugshot photo of Truett. "Major, for now I'm going to revisit the folks Arthur interviewed. They've had plenty of time to work this thing over in their minds. The more thought they give it, the more they might remember. We'll see."

Hightower continued as if delivering a classroom lecture. "After I talk to those folks I'm going to work on Truett. I hope I'll get his attention enough that I won't need Evans or Williams. Could be one of them will call on me when they find out I'm talking with the other. I've found it common for one perpetrator to keep quiet, sometimes two, but three's a crowd. When you have three men involved in something like this, at least one will become suspicious of the others. When a man's life is at stake, who knows." Hightower looked up at Hutchins. "That's all I've got for now, gentlemen. Thanks for making yourselves available, I'm sure I'll be calling on you going forward."

Although leads had been established, Hightower was determined to work from a clean slate, not relying on prior investigation. He spent the next several months interviewing every witness whose name appeared in the files. He wanted to hear for himself what they had to say. "Better to look a man in his face while he's talking than read his words secondhand from a file cabinet," Hightower said.

After re-interviewing the witnesses, Hightower found each story remained as originally told to Captain Hutchins. However, he found two men of particular interest: M. C. Perry and one other man, identified but never interviewed, Edward Willing, the name on the parts receipt Wade Truett showed Arthur Hutchins at his garage in Hartsville, South Carolina.

In late February, U. S. Marshals escorted M. C. Perry from the Atlanta Federal Penitentiary to GBI headquarters for questioning. Perry was seated inside Hightower's office when the agent came through the door.

"Mr. Perry, I'm Robert Hightower. I had you brought here today to talk about the three policemen murdered in Gwinnett County last April."

"Mister, you're a little late, 'cause I already told everything I knowed about it to Homer Lee Cheek with the DeKalb County Sheriff's department."

"I know that, Mr. Perry, but how about you telling me?"

"I don't care for you or nobody else bothering me no more about that thing. Like I said, go talk to Mr. Cheek, 'cause I'm sure tired of all y'all's questions."

"Oh you are, are you? Okay, have it your way. But listen, since you're already here, let me ask you this. Did you have anything to do with the murder of those three police officers?"

"No! I ain't had nothing to do with it! I done told Mr. Cheek and the others I don't know how many times. Now, here you are asking me the same questions, but this time I ain't gonna bother, 'cause you won't believe my answers no way. You want anything out of me, get me a lawyer. I know my rights."

"Relax, M. C. It just so happens I believe what you told Mr. Cheek. I don't think you had anything to do with the murders either, and you're correct in that you have the right to an attorney present for any questioning, but you'll have no problems here with me."

"You're goddamn right about that, 'cause I didn't have nothing to do with none of it! Makes me mad myself just thinking about what they done to them policemen."

"About what who done to those policemen, M. C.? Who is they?"

"Y'all know who!"

"No, I don't, but if you're so mad about what happened, then maybe you can tell me. Of course that's only if you feel like talking just between us." Hightower tilted a casual but effective smile toward Perry.

"Oh hell, Mr. Hightower, you know who. I'm sure I ain't telling you nothing you don't already know. Hell, man, everybody in the whole damn county knows. Was Alex Evans, Venson Williams, and I'm thinking that damn little punk-ass partner of his, Wade Truett. That little weasel."

"You're thinking?"

"Hell, yes, same as everybody else."

"The first Monday after the murders I believe you told Mr. Cheek about how Venson Williams and then Alex Evans had asked you to find a sixty-three Oldsmobile for them."

"Right, but—"

"But you told Alex that you wouldn't do it for Venson because he owed you money."

"That's right. Son of a bitch never did pay what he owed me."

"When you said you wouldn't do such a thing for Venson because he wouldn't pay, it was money he owed you from the last car you stole for him, isn't that why you weren't going to do it anymore?"

"That's why."

"You stole cars for Venson before."

"Yeah, three or four, something along in there."

"M. C., did you have any further contact with either Alex Evans or Venson Williams after you first spoke about this to Detective Cheek?"

"That's a good question. I ain't never told nobody this, Mr. Hightower, 'cause ain't nobody ever asked, but I guess it was about a week after it happened that I was up at Red's Service Station in Buford. Me and my wife stopped there on our way to my uncle's house. Well Alex and his wife come up there, and we was all reading the paper about how this nut job Bozo Powell was telling the news people he had got in the middle of the killers that night and was in a gunfight with 'em and got shot trying to stop 'em. Turns out the stupid idiot shot his own self in the leg. Did so thinking everybody would believe him about being some kind of hero. It was all a load of garbage. He was just trying to impress his ol' lady who'd kicked his drunk ass out of their house for the last time. But he wanted back, like, you know, was trying to get back on her good side. Then all of a sudden they's all claiming something another that he's the one who done it, killed those policemen. Anyways, me and Alex got through reading the paper. When I carried it to my wife, I looked at Alex sitting on the ice cream box and said, 'What is Bozo trying to do, get a bunch of publicity out of this?' Alex said he figured they had the one who done it. I told him if I wanted to know who done it, I would see his and my friend."

"You told that to Alex Evans?"

"Yeah, told that to Alex."

"What happened next?"

"He got mad as hell. Jumped down off the ice cream box and told me if I thought I knowed anything about it to keep my damn mouth shut. He kept getting more madder and then started punching me in the chest, pushing me back against the counter."

"Just out of curiosity, M. C., do you remember how he was dressed, what he was wearing?"

"Yeah, if it matters any, he was dressed in corduroy. Had on a brown hat. Had a .38 snub nose tucked in his belt."

"What happened after he told you to keep your mouth shut?"

"Well, like I said, he was real mad. I didn't know what he would do next, so I grabbed my old lady and got the hell out of there fast as I could."

"Tell me again what day you think it was."

"I can tell you the exact day. Thursday, April twenty-third. I remember 'cause the next week I turned in. That was the last time I was over to Red's. Thursday the twenty-third."

"M. C., I'll be seeing you again, we'll talk more about this. I'll probably have Mr. Reid Merritt, Gwinnett County solicitor with me. You okay with that?"

Hightower spoke cordially to Perry, as if to suggest a mutual partnership had evolved between them.

"Yeah, I know Mr. Merritt. He's all right. Honestly, if anything, I don't care what happens to these guys. See, I knowed Jerry Everett. Ralph Davis too. Mr. Hightower, them boys didn't need to go like that, not over a stolen car they didn't."

Later that evening Hightower arranged a next-day meeting with Edward Willing. Willing was the owner of B & W Wrecking Company in Graniteville, South Carolina, fourteen miles east over the Georgia line and 115 miles west of Hartsville. The fresh-air two-lane drive between endless rolls of quiet farmland gave the agent his first break in a while from the city clamor. Mid-morning Hightower pulled into the wrecking yard and spotted a man of fireplug proportions. He wore a crisp fitted company uniform. Above his honest smiling face tilted a baseball cap marked with touches of salvage-yard grime atop and under its bill.

Hightower, himself smiling, called out. "Hey, you Mr. Willing?"

"No, sir, they called my daddy Mr. Willing. Folks just call me Eddy. You the Georgia lawman who phoned last night?"

"That'd be me. Robert Hightower, Eddy. Thanks for seeing me on such short notice. Man, that's a pretty drive out here from Atlanta."

"Atlanta, huh? Been a while since I was out that way. Heard it's busting out of its seams. What can I do for you, sir?"

"I've got some pictures here I'd like you to look at, if you don't mind."

Willing happily obliged. "Don't mind at all. But, first, what say we get inside, out of this hot sun, if you don't mind?"

Both men entered the yard's small front office. Hightower removed three pictures from his briefcase and spread them side by side on the parts counter. The pictures were prison mugshots, each identified only by numbers but belonging to Alex S. Evans, Wade Levi Truett, and Venson Eugene Williams.

"Eddy, take a look here and tell me if you recognize any of these faces."

Willing removed his hat and rubbed his eyes. "Let's see what you got." He thumped his finger on Evans' picture. "Nope, don't believe I ever seen this fella here." He thumped Truett's. "This fella looks kinda familiar. Can't place him right at this moment, but I might've seen him somewheres before." He barely glanced at the third picture. "This one here is Venson Williams. Venson, Eugene, whatever; goes by both, but ain't no doubt that's him."

"No doubt?"

"No, sir, ain't no doubt about it."

"Recall the last time you seen him?"

"Be last...I want to say...last October, thereabouts. Came in here wanting a duplicate receipt for some body panels he bought further back in April."

"Alone by himself, or was there anybody with him?"

"Was another fella with him, but he stayed in the car; didn't come inside."

"You know who that other fella was?"

"Nope, sure don't."

"If you would, Eddy, tell me all about what took place, best as you remember."

"Well, he came here last April, bought...wait a minute, let me get 'em for you." Willing retrieved paperwork from the office file cabinet. "Here, see these receipts?"

"Yeah."

"This here's the original, dated April twenty-fourth. He bought a nineteen sixty-three Oldsmobile left quarter, top, and left door. Paid a hundred seventy-five dollars, plus five dollars and twenty-five cents tax, total of a hundred eighty dollars and twenty-five cents. It's all right here. Then he comes back, I wanna say around October, wanting another receipt for them parts he bought. Said he lost the original. Well, I figured he needed it for his books, so I told him to wait a minute, I'd have to get it from the office, pull the date off it, 'cause I didn't remember exactly. Venson tells me he ain't got no time to wait, and asked if I would just make out a new receipt. Said he remembered the date, April fourth, and parts too. Well, as he told me, he was in a hurry, so I just did what he said. Made no difference to me. I kinda laughed, though. Told him he had a better memory than me to recollect all that.

"He said he remembered so good because they was trying to fix him to them three Georgia policemen who got killed. Well, that caught me by surprise, so I asked how's that? He said they was trying to blame him for their murders, but he didn't need no stolen car 'cause he had already bought parts from me before all that happened. I didn't know what the hell he was talking about till later that day. I started looking for this original receipt in one of my old books, and sure enough, there it was, but it wasn't right about the date he gave me. The real date was April twenty-fourth, not April fourth. That's about all I can tell you, but let me ask you a question. You figure he had something to do with it?"

"I don't know."

"You say." Willing's mouth spread into a doubtful grin. "But I don't think you'd have come from Atlanta all the way out here to little old Graniteville because you don't know. You look way too smart to do that, huh?"

"I can't really speak much to that, but you're pretty perceptive, Eddy. Sure are."

Hightower was pleased with what the muscular man told him. "By the way, Eddy, there's something else I'd like to ask, just out of curiosity, you understand. Would you say stealing cars is big business?"

"I reckon it is, but not around here. Least not that I know of, and I think I would. See, Daddy died in forty-three, so you could say I raised myself selling cars and parts out of this yard. Ain't much hardly gets past me, if you know what I mean. Probably back in your neck of the woods, the big city, I would say it is, yeah, but not around here, they ain't."

"That right?"

"Mr. Hightower, let me put it like this: the law's between me and every car I tow. In this office I've got full paperwork for every wreck you see out there in that yard. To the best of my knowledge, I ain't never took in no stolen car. Folks around here know me. They know I don't have nothing to do with that kind of business. My books are all here for you to check if you want."

"Oh no, no, that won't be necessary, Eddy. I believe you. You don't need to show me anything. Besides, you've already given me your time, and I sure do appreciate it."

In no particular hurry, Hightower drove at a leisurely pace back to Atlanta, confident that solving Georgia's biggest crime was in his control. Eddy's story showed conspiracy. It might not be the smoking gun, but no doubt it smacked of conspiracy through coverup. In fact it showed it on the front end with Perry's story about stealing the Olds and now on the back end with Willing's story. There was only one piece of the puzzle left to find, an eyewitness. It was time to pull his ace card. Time to put the squeeze on Wade Truett.

Late April 1965, one year after the murders, inside the Federal Corrections Institution, Tallahassee, Florida, two guards took Wade Levi Truett from his cell to the lawyer's consultation room, a twelve-foot by twelve-foot windowless cinderblock room painted beige and containing three wood chairs placed around a circular table. Truett sat against the back wall facing the door.

Without knocking, Hightower barged through the door intending to startle Truett with his abrupt entrance. It worked. The tall agent's dark eyes had a cold steeliness, a cool confident gaze, not at all urgent. Standing just inside the room he calmly surveyed its bare ambiance. He closed the door while greeting the inmate. "Wade Truett, I'm Robert Hightower with the Georgia Bureau of Investigation." His spur-of-the-moment manner promptly kicked in. "Whoa! It's hotter than hell in here. Ain't you hot?"

Truett, unsettled from Hightower's abrupt entrance, said, "No. Well, I don't know, maybe a little."

"Man, the last time I've been this hot in a prison was Reidsville State Penitentiary. I was in that room we call the Chamber of Justice. I'm sure y'all call it something different in here. I'll bet it was a hundred degrees if anything." He shook his head. "They've got to do something about that. To see a man meet his death in those conditions, boy, that was tough. I swear I must've sweated out five pounds in there that day." He slowly glowed a devilish grin while staring at the inmate. "I don't mean in any way to come off callous about it. I saw a John Wayne picture once where this young gun-slinging punk called out the Duke to prove he was gonna be the new bad dog in town. Wayne says to him, 'Son, you ever watched a man die? Well, as many as I have, it ain't so much fun anymore.' I've come to understand what he meant by that. Watching a man die, it ain't so much fun anymore. You see, Wade, I serve the state as an official witness to executions. I've got no choice; I have to be there when called. It's part of my job."

Hightower locked eyes with the inmate as he took a seat at the table. "Hey, you ever seen how it works?"

"No."

"Brother, let me tell you, it's intense." The tall, athletic Georgia agent began a second-person trip as if it were prophecy. "The process starts in your cell. The prison chaplain comes in to talk, if you want. Most do. It's a calming time while he talks because a few minutes afterwards the orderlies come in and shave off all your hair. That's the easy part. From there on, it gets real uncomfortable real fast. One of the orderlies has to stuff your rectum full of cotton. Very unpleasant! They usually wait till the last minute for that, but one way or the other it has to be done. Keeps you from messing yourself and the electric chair during the procedure."

He shook his head as if clearing the thought from his mind. "Anyway, next thing you know the chaplain motions for the guards. He tells you, 'Wade, it's time. We gotta take the walk.' As you're heading to the death chamber, he recites The Lord's Prayer. He'll repeat it several times. When you get there, guards open the door and bring you inside. Sometimes the condemned man comes in all calm and cool. He's the tough son of a bitch who doesn't give a damn about nothing, not even his own sorry ass. Heartless bastard figured for what he'd done, he was gonna get it anyhow, sooner or later. I've also seen it go to the extreme where a man comes in kicking and screaming, crying out for Jesus. Fights it all the way till the guards sit him in the chair. They wrap leather belts around your arms, top and bottom of your legs, waist, chest, and forehead. I promise, you ain't going nowhere further in this life after those straps get buckled down."

Hightower raised an eyebrow and nodded his head. He continued the sequence of events. "The guards leave the chamber, and from inside the witness room this fella slides open a curtain uncovering a glass window. Those there to witness the execution get their first look at you sitting in that chair. Now that's a real eye opener, because right then they're thinking *Oh, dear Lord, I'm going to watch this man put to his death.* I've seen a time or two where one will leave before it starts. Seeing you all strapped up like that is plenty enough to satisfy their curiosity. They don't need to see anymore. Now most will stay, but they'll be pretty scared about it all. Looking around at everything. I mean you gotta know where they'll be come Sunday morning!

"At that point I used to ask the condemned man if he had any last words he'd like to say, but as I said, 'used to.' I stopped that step in the procedure. Once, this guy, he's sitting in the chair, asked me to come closer so he could whisper something in my ear. Me being the nice guy I am, I did as he asked. The S.O.B spit in my face. How could I have been so naive? Yeah, I stopped doing that. Oh, sorry, Wade, sometimes I get a bit off track. Let's see, where were we?" Hightower tilted his head back and rubbed his chin. "Oh yeah, right. They put a wet sponge on top of your head then strap a metal skull cap over the sponge. Now they're moving along pretty quick here. Next thing is they put a rubber block between your teeth. It's got a hole in it so you can breathe.

"Chaplain stands next to you asking the Lord to forgive you of all your sinful transgressions, and then he steps out of the room. There's nobody in the room with you at that point. That's another bad thing about all this, man, dying all alone. Oh, you can see people watching through the glass partition, reporters, victim's families, but still, you're all alone when you die. I've often wondered what could be going through a man's mind at a time like that. Sometimes I've thought, we ought to give 'em some kind of countdown, like three, two, one, but that's just me.

"Anyway, they pull the switch. It's a quick response, I'll tell you that. When those volts hit, you shake so hard you'd think the chair was gonna walk the floor. I've seen it go quick and I've seen it go all wrong. Oh God, can it ever go wrong. This old boy been on death row a good while had one hell of a time with it. A few seconds into the deal his fingernails melt off his fingertips. Man, it got ugly! Puffs of white smoke shot out of his ears. His mouth was blowing white foam out the breathing hole in that rubber block and then his head caught on fire. I could actually see fire coming out from under the metal cap. Now this is a good twenty, twenty-five seconds after they threw the switch. He was still jerking and smoking, screaming, I'm sure, the way that foam was coming out in spurts.

"You've got big cotton balls taped tight over your eyes so they don't pop out from the pressure, but still, even with all that cotton, they explode to where blood runs down under each eye. Now that's ugly.

"Usually about this time I'll look over to the family, the victim's family. They're allowed to watch if they want. Lot of 'em do. They want to see justice for themselves, firsthand. Even with the hatred they hold for the condemned man, no matter how much you prepare them, they'll cringe at the sight. Some bow their heads in prayer. Some scream. I've seen a time or two where they got sick to their stomach, actually threw up.

"Anyway, they keep the electricity flowing for thirty seconds before it's finally over, most of the time. Prison doctor comes in checking for a pulse. He either nods for yes or shakes his head for no. If no, he leaves the room and they pull the switch a second time. I've always figured, there is no way you're going to live through that first time, right? Like getting hit by a thirty-second lightning bolt. Splits you in half. But more often than you'd think, they pull it again. And as long as that electricity is hitting you, there's gonna be more smoke, spew, and jerking about. It's just the power of electricity. You're already long dead.

"After it's all over the curtains are drawn before the guards unstrap your body from the chair. They just let you flop down to the floor and then roll you onto the stretcher and haul you off. I'll speak to the victim's family briefly. Most of the time they have blank stares from what they just saw. They take no joy from it. I guarantee they'll never forget it. Moments before, this man walked into the death chamber a perfectly healthy human being. Now he's dead. It's tough on everybody, but that's how our system works.

"Truth be told there is one person who comes out a winner. That's the dead guy. Hell, he's gone. He doesn't have to bear responsibility anymore. But everybody else he leaves behind does, for the rest of their lives. When a man is put to death, his family walks under a dark cloud forever. Wherever they go there's a feeling that someone's looking at them, watching, talking behind their backs. Brother, that kind of existence will make the sane go crazy. As I look at who he's left behind, I see nothing but victims. That's what he left behind, nothing but victims. Nobody wins except for him. Everybody else loses.

"I'm sure you've figured out by now there's no love lost between me and the deceased. Had it coming, I figure. But I will say this. It's seeing his folks that tears my heart out. Of course your family is not allowed to watch your execution, so you don't need to worry about that. The prison has a special room for them. They set it up nice, try to make it comfortable. Twenty minutes after it's all over, they'll roll you in so any of your family who's there can spend a few minutes with you, if they want. Prison doctor covers you in a white sheet up to your neck and wraps the top of your head in cotton gauze, but your family is able to see your face. Doc gives it a quick cleaning, but there's always going to be some telltale bruising. Can't hardly do much about that. Course the prison chaplain will come in with you, say a prayer for anyone there. Usually a man's mother is there, but not his daddy. He's too ashamed. He feels a failure, raised his son only to have our social order put him to death.

"I'm the sorry bastard that comes in to tell his mother it's time to go. She can either have your body or let the prison have it. It hurts me to see what that does to a mother, see her cry like that. Breaks my heart.

"There are times when I can't help but think, that could've been my mother. Maybe if I'd taken a left instead of taken a right. Zigged instead of zagged. Maybe not even my fault. Could've just been in the wrong place at the wrong time. You know, got caught up with the wrong crowd and all. That could happen to any of us. It's all about decisions, Wade.. That's what our lives are made of. In the end did we make the right decisions? Sometimes you can't take it back but, fortunately, sometimes we get a second chance at making the right decision. It can happen. You just gotta know the opportunity when it comes. Grab hold of it.

"Oh no, look what I've done. Wade, I'm sorry, I got so carried away with my jabbering that just now I realized I've got a meeting with Warden Knowlton. I'll let the guards know we're finished, come get you out of this oven. You take care, okay?"

Hightower excused himself, left the room, and closed the door behind him. He also left Truett hanging in uncertainty with no hint of another meeting. In the hallway Hightower told the guards, "Let the boy sit in there ten or so minutes before you take him back to his cell. Give him time to think about what I said."

Inside the room, Truett stared at the closed door. He wondered, "What in the hell just happened?" He envisioned his execution, his funeral, his gravestone. "Venson was right. They're gonna strap us in that electric chair."

The following morning the previous day's unnerving repeated itself. Two guards appeared in front of Wade's cell. "Inmate Truett, get up. We're taking a little walk. Let's go!" He was escorted back to the lawyers room where again Hightower, unannounced, barged through the gray door. The GBI agent set his scuffed brown leather briefcase on top of the table, pulled up a chair, and sat directly across from Truett. The inmate looked markedly more haggard than the day before. Obviously Hightower's impressive Chamber of Justice narrative had, as intended, added to the prisoner's distress.

"Good morning, Wade. How'd you sleep last night?"

"Not so good."

"Is that right? Me, I slept like a baby."

Hightower exhibited relaxed friendliness. "Had dinner at Warden Knowlton's house last night. Brother, I'm here to tell you, he's one lucky man for sure. That wife of his can cook a meal like you wouldn't believe. Beef pot roast, potatoes, carrots, sweet Vidalia onions; thought I'd bust. Then she brings in an apple pie. Whole thing, straight from the oven. Oh Lord, I'm still hurting. After dinner we sat in his den where he pulled out these Cuban cigars and the smoothest sippin' brandy I've ever had. We talked about this and that, prison stuff mostly. He tells me you're hardly eating. I know prison food isn't exactly fine French cuisine, but still, I've eaten it a time or two. Had no problem keeping it down. For a fact, I've sure had worse. Warden also tells me you're not taking your yard time either. Course I can't much blame you for that, what with all those convicts out there." He snorted a soft chuckle. "They're not exactly here for singing too loud in church, right?"

"No, sir." Truett said.

"Tell me, Wade, what's going on? Something heavy on your mind?"

"I've been thinking about what you said. You believe I was somehow involved with those police murders in Gwinnett County, don't you?"

"Yes, Wade, I do. Why don't you tell me about it?" Hightower's dark brown eyes cast no emotion. He presented the ghostly face of authority, the life-or-death kind, able to stand between Truett and that Chamber of Justice.

"I swear to God I didn't shoot any of those policemen. All I wanted to do was get out of there."

Truett stared at the floor and shook his head.

"I never figured they'd kill 'em. Nobody said nothing about that. I thought they was just gonna handcuff 'em to a tree and leave. Those policemen didn't know me or Venson. We could've been back to South Carolina by morning. They'd a never have found us in South Carolina, but..." horror filled his eyes. "I heard what sounded like firecrackers. Wasn't till I got down that hill I seen they were shooting 'em."

Although excited, Hightower showed no reaction. Instead he remained silent.

Truett continued, "They just kept shooting."

Leaning close-in to the inmate's side, Hightower softly asked, "Who was shooting them, Wade?"

"They were! Alex and Venson." Truett's fear changed to anger. "The policemen were already laying on the ground when I got down there. That's when I seen Alex pointing his flashlight and Venson leaning over one of 'em and shooting him two or three times. I didn't know they were gonna kill 'em." The prisoner laid his head on the table and cried. "I swear to God I didn't know."

Behind his blank stare, Hightower rejoiced. There it is! I got these bastards. The year-long sluggish investigation just hit full speed. The lawman not only had his eyewitness, but an actual participant. Waiting a triumphant few moments, Hightower insisted, "Wade, sit up, take a deep breath, and tell me again who you saw shoot those officers."

"Venson Williams and Alex Evans. I know what you're thinking. You're thinking I'm lying, but it was Alex and Venson who put 'em in that Oldsmobile and drove off. I stayed behind moving their car to where it wouldn't be seen. You gotta believe me. I didn't know they were gonna kill 'em."

Next to the closed door stood a small tray table. On it sat a nearly full pitcher of water and several paper cups. Hightower filled one, placed it in front of Truett and said, "Keep going."

"I backed the police car into them woods, run out to the road, got in my car, and followed after the Olds. They'd already gone over to the other side of that hill. I couldn't see where. It was real dark, but as I come down, I heard what sounded like a nickel pack of firecrackers all lit at one time, the way they go off. When I got to where the road flattens, there was the Oldsmobile. I parked right in behind, got out, and stepped up on a little bank and took four or five steps, wasn't very far. That's when I seen in the woods Alex shining his flashlight and Venson leaning over the middle one, taking bullets from the back of his belt. He loaded a gun Alex gave him and shot one of the policemen straight in his face, two or three times. Looked to me they was already dead, but that one Venson shot was making a gurgling noise, so I guess he shot him again to make sure."

"What do you mean, gurgling noise?"

"The sound he was making, I say gurgling 'cause it reminded me of when I was a boy whenever my daddy killed a hog. Hit it in the head with an axe, and it snorted blood out its nose, making a gurgling sound, same as I heard coming from that policeman. I don't guess I'll ever get over that sound. It stopped when Venson shot him."

"You're telling me you saw Venson Williams shoot one of the policemen two or three times?"

"Was either two or three times, I can't say for sure, but yes, sir."

"Did you see Alex Evans shoot any of the policemen?"

"No, sir, I only seen Venson shoot the one police-man, but I figured Alex must've too, 'cause he had all the guns."

"You said those three policemen didn't know you or Venson. Is that right?"

"Yes, sir. Didn't know me, and I doubt Venson. But Alex...they seemed to know him pretty good."

"What makes you say that?"

"By the way they were all talking to one another. In fact, they all seemed to know each other real good, call-ing first names."

"Could you hear what they were talking about?"

"The younger officer was mad and talking to Alex in a raised voice. I was plenty scared. Didn't pay no atten-tion to whatever else they was saying."

Hightower allowed Truett a moment to clear his nerves. He offered Truett coffee and cigarettes as a re-ward for his cooperation. As Truett lit his second cig-arette, Hightower removed from his briefcase a yellow legal pad and two ballpoint pens and sat the case on the floor beside his chair. "All right, Wade, start from the be-ginning and tell me what led you and Venson to Atlanta April sixteenth of last year." He stared at the inmate. "I'm listening."

Truett had calmed and was eager to tell his story. "Me and Venson were in Hartsville, South Carolina. We got us a shop there. Venson bought this salvaged car, a six-ty-three Olds coupe, from a yard over in Atlanta. Thing was wrecked all to hell. Couldn't fix it without using an-other car for parts and couldn't buy another car 'cause we didn't have no money. Venson had asked M.C. Perry to find him a car, but M.C. wouldn't do it. So Venson asked Alex Evans if he'd find one for us to steal. A few days later he calls and said he found what we were looking for. We left Hartsville next day, mid-morning. Come straight to Atlanta. Venson was drivin 'cause he knows the roads there. I don't. First stop we make is Leroy Thomas' house near Lawrenceville. Leroy and Venson are buddies. Didn't stay long, thirty minutes I'd say."

Truett recalled that day from a full year before. "Drove up Beaver Ruin Road to an Esso Fleet next to the expressway. Bought cigarettes and some beer. Venson tried calling Alex but couldn't get him, so we went on to Atlanta, Joe Cotton's Drive-In, corner of Lee and White-hall streets. This was, I'm guessing, something around seven, eight o'clock abouts. Venson tried callin Alex again and still couldn't get him. Left a message with somebody there. Said, 'Tell him Slim called and will call back later.' Lots of people call him Slim, he's kind of tall. We drove around Atlanta a while, through some apartments, looking for this car, but never did find it. I was a little hungry so we come back to Joe Cotton's. That's when Venson finally got hold of Alex, something like nine, ten o'clock. Said, 'We're going to meet him.' I don't know the exact route, but we left Atlanta and came back out the expressway toward Lawrenceville. It was somewhere on Highway Twenty-three toward Buford or Gainesville. Up that road a piece there's an old lodge or Moose Club on the right. Got an asphalt drive up front. Wasn't nobody there; least no lights was on. Alex, just all of a sudden, is standing next to our car. I got in the backseat and he sat up front with Venson.

"We came out from there heading back to Atlanta, probably around ten, eleven thirty. I never thought much about time that night. Alex, he's given directions to Venson on where to go, Briarcliff and Lavista Roads. We pulled in to some apartments, and sure enough there's a sixty-three maroon Olds eighty-eight, just like the one we had in Hartsville. We park about a hundred feet away. From there Alex and Venson walked to the car. Venson jacked the driver door and both got in. Alex, he's driving. He's the only one knows where we're going. They came past me and got on the expressway, and I followed. Alex is going pretty good, 'cause I'm having trouble keeping up."

Hightower glanced up from his notes. "Describe the car you were driving."

"Sixty-two Chevy Super Sport Impala, white, white-beige convertible top. Got a big-block motor in it."

"Go on."

"They got off the expressway at Beaver Ruin Road, drove for about a mile, still a good ways ahead of me. At first I couldn't tell exactly where, till I pass where he turned off. That's when I seen brake lights up the hill so I done a U-turn and started up that dirt road. Drove past a house there on the right. Didn't have no lights on and wasn't nobody watching, far as I could tell. Dog barking loud down that way, but exactly from where I don't know. I pulled up close behind the Oldsmobile, and by the time I parked they were already changing out the ignition switch. The plan was for Venson to change out the switch with one that's got a key, and I was gonna change out the license plate with a South Carolina dealer tag that's got a registration. That way if a trooper pulled us over, the car's got a normal switch and the tag matches the registration. Usually cops just let you go, not thinking twice it's stoled.

"We was gonna drive straight through the night and be back in Hartsville by morning.

"I grabbed a couple tools and had my parking lights on so I could see. Wasn't none of us in no hurry. We hadn't been there no more than a few minutes before I had the tag off but not yet put the dealer tag on, when I seen headlights shining up from over the other side of that hill. I could tell they were coming our way. I had left my door open, and with the road being so narrow can't but one car go through at a time. I walked back to close it, figuring whoever it was would just go on by, but then the red bubble light came on, and I knew right away it was the law."

Truett rubbed his hands. His face twitched and his voice stuttered before he paused to swallow.

Hightower interrupted the pause with a question. "You said you had taken the Oldsmobile's license plate off. What did you do with it?"

"Slung it out in that field or pasture alongside the road where we was parked."

"One other thing, you told me earlier you backed the police car into the woods. Remember what you did with its keys?"

"When I got out I guess I just threw 'em in the woods. I don't...I was so nervous, I don't remember."

The keys were not important, but the license plate, if found, would prove to be irrefutable evidence and confirm Truett's presence at the crime scene.

"Listen, let me tell you something. I still see it just like...just like it's frozen in the back of my brain. It's all the time. It don't stop, not day or night. This whole thing, just ain't no end to it."

"All right, Wade. Take a deep breath."

"No, I'm...I don't wanna talk no more. I done told you what happened. I don't wanna talk about it no more."

"All done?"

"Far as I'm concerned, yes, sir."

"So you figure it's all over now?"

"I reckon not. I don't think it ever will be, least not as long as I'm alive. But for now, can we just say it is?"

"Yeah, that's okay. I understand. We'll stop right here. But you know what? I'll let you in on a little secret." Hightower coolly began packing his briefcase. "You and me, the two of us, we have something in common. It's like this. We both need each other's help, and for your part, there's maybe a chance, a good chance, I can keep you out of that chair. Tell you why: I've been looking at this thing for a while now, and I already knew a good bit about what you just told me. It matches. Now I'm going to look at the rest of what I didn't know. If it matches, we might can make a deal. Course if it doesn't..." Hightower clamped the locks on his briefcase, stood up, and turned toward the door. "If it doesn't, there won't be any deal to make." The GBI agent opened the door to leave.

Truett shouted, "Hey, where you going? What about me?"

Hightower turned, faced the inmate. "What about you? The guards are gonna take you back to your cell. Get yourself packed, we're going to Atlanta, leaving as soon as I clear it with Warden Knowlton."

"Atlanta? Why?"

Hightower leaned down, bracing both arms on the table. He stared coldly into Truett's face, only inches away. "Fix your eyes right here to mine. Did you shoot any of those police officers?"

"I swear, as God is my witness, Mr. Hightower, I did not shoot any of those policemen. I couldn't ever do nothing like that."

"I sure hope that's so, because, if what you're telling me pans out, I'm gonna be the best friend you ever had, but if I find otherwise, especially if you shot any of those officers, you'll be praying inside that room I talked about yesterday. I'll personally strap you in that chair and pull the switch myself. That's a fact. Hear me?"

"Yes, sir, I hear you. I just hope you hear me." Truett dropped his head. "I'm real scared, Mr. Hightower."

"I'd say you have good reason to be. Get your gear."

While the guards escorted Truett back to his cell, Hightower met with Warden Knowlton in his office. "Warden, I'm taking inmate Truett back to Atlanta as my prime witness for the triple police murders in Gwinnett County. I'd like to leave as soon as possible, if that's okay with you."

"Yeah, that'll be fine. Give me about thirty minutes. We'll have all the paperwork done by then."

"I appreciate it, Warden. Mind if I use your phone?"

"No, not at all."

The prison switchboard put a call through to Barney Ragsdale.

Hightower gushed, "Major, I just got a confession out of Wade Truett. Told me he was on that dirt road, all right; Alex Evans and Venson Williams, too. Said he wasn't involved. Evans and Williams did the shooting. I believe it. I'm bringing him with me back to Atlanta. Find a private cell to put him in; we don't want to mix him with other inmates. And if you would, call Lieutenant Stanley, have him meet me at Arc Road tomorrow morning, say around eight thirty. Tell him to bring a set of crime scene photos for reference. And have the sheriff from Gwinnett out there too. Have him bring a dozen or so of his farm prisoners with him. I've got to do some scrubbing around in a pasture out there. Make it same time as Stanley. You might want to go ahead and give Mr. Merritt a call, let him know. Ball's in his court now, he can have Truett."

"Why hell yes, Bob! But before we get all excited with Reid, you think Truett's gonna cooperate?"

"I'll bet his life on it."

"That's a risky bet, Hightower."

"Yeah, well, I guess you could say everything's risky with this confession, but I don't see that you've got any other choice, do you? Truett's not stupid, Major. He's damn scared, and hell, I don't blame him. Pinning Evans and Williams without a conviction might as well be his death sentence. Those boys will chain him behind a pickup truck and drag his dead corpse till there's nothing left. He knows that, so you're asking me if he'll cooperate? Well, I believe he's telling the truth, and I bet I can prove it, but Merritt's gonna have to convince him of that conviction. And then to get him on that witness stand he'll need to promise something. The way I figure it, that something is gonna have to be total immunity. I've gone so far as dangle it in front of him, but of course Reid will have to approve it, and Major, the way y'all been getting your asses chewed on, I bet he'll do it. If I was you, I'd take that bet."

"Yeah, you're right, I'll take it."

Hightower drove Truett back to Atlanta, arriving late that afternoon. Georgia state troopers took custody of the prisoner and delivered him to a private cell inside the Fulton County Jailhouse. Director Ragsdale, with Solicitor Merritt, eagerly waited inside the Gwinnett Room for the lead agent. Both men listened as Hightower retold Truett's confession.

Twenty miles north of downtown Atlanta, Arc Road remained the same as twelve months earlier. Its dust plumes still swirled and then settled without notice, except for the solemn gaze up its hill by passing motorists on Beaver Ruin, their intensity of the horror little changed a year later.

☙

GBI agent Robert Hightower parked alongside Lieutenant Stanley's car, blocking the road's south entrance.
The Gwinnett County sheriff stood nearby with ten
county farm prisoners huddled together. All wore heavily
starched white uniforms with unmistakable shoulder-to-
shoe blue stripes. One shotgun-armed deputy held their
undivided attention. Two State Patrol cruisers straddled
Beaver Ruin Road as four troopers stood at the entrance
of Arc Road ensuring the morning search would go without interruption from curiosity seekers.

Hightower stepped out of his car and found Lieutenant Stanley holding a cigarette while talking to the
troopers. Hightower nodded and said, "Good morning,
Lieutenant. I appreciate you coming out on such short
notice." Grinning his typical prelude to wisdom, Hightower informed his tall partner, "Hasn't anybody ever
told you smoking those things will stunt your growth?"

Stanley responded in a cheerless voice. "I heard you
been a busy boy. Also heard tell you got a confession out
of Truett. That right?"

"That's right. He was here. Told me he didn't do any
of the shooting, though. Evans and Williams did."

"My ass! You don't believe that crock of bull do you?"

"Actually, Lieutenant, I do. But, one way or the other, we're gonna find out if I'm right or if I'm wrong."

The lead agent took a long, penetrating look at the
place central to his investigation. "It's about time I came
out here myself. Should be evidence here that'll make me
sure, if we find what Truett says we'll find. At the very
least it'll convince me whether he was here that night
or not. If we don't find it, it'll make me look like a fool,
I know. Boy gave me no reason to believe otherwise,

though. I don't think he's lying. And I don't think he shot any of those officers either."

"You prove he didn't shoot any of those officers, and I'll recommend you for agent of the year."

"Well, it's not over yet. Mr. Merritt has a long way to go. We've all got a long way to go. So far I've just taken what y'all already had and run with it. I wouldn't say that qualifies me for agent of the year. Let's get these county farm boys to work. Show me where you remember the Oldsmobile's papers were found."

The Lieutenant's gaze wandered up then down the rutted dirt course of Arc Road. "I remember this godamn place like it was yesterday." He followed his stare by pointing. "Our boys were found lying face down in them woods over that hill there, all handcuffed together. Damndest thing you ever did see. Hardly believe your own eyes, seeing something like that. Troopers just standing in a daze. Locals walking wherever they damn well pleased." Stanley appeared still agitated. "Wasn't nobody doing their job! Hell, they were all in shock. I guess we all were. Seeing them boys all shot to pieces, all tore up like that. Knew from the start was with their own guns. I hate this place." Stanley shook his head. "That day...that night...Lord, I'll never forget that night. We'd all met at City Hall in Lawrenceville. Lowell Conner was telling everybody. Said he and his boys was gonna find the killers and bring fair justice for those officers. Assistant Chief up here in Gwinnett told Conner in as many words to go suck eggs. Said if he finds 'em first, he was gonna hang the bastards from a rope. Let 'em dangle till their eyeballs popped out. Boy, I tell you every cop in Atlanta felt the same way."

Hightower nodded. "I believe I would've told Conner likewise." Hightower struck a serious gaze at the lieutenant. "But now that we got the bastards first, I'm not gonna hang 'em. Gonna fry 'em. Take that as the Gospel Truth to Almighty Conner!"

The two men walked up the long hill on Arc Road and stopped just shy of its crest. Count, the Mills family dog, trotted out from his sentinel post. His tail wagged with friendship; he cocked his head with curiosity. He was a welcome interruption to the morning's dire task; they appeared to him a welcome difference to his usual boredom.

After flipping through the crime scene photos, Lieutenant Stanley paused. "This area right about here is where it all started. Tire marks. Footprints." He pointed into the side ditch. "Gwinnett chief found the Oldsmobile papers and two blackjacks down in there."

Hightower shouted to the county-farm prisoners. "All right, men, I'm looking for an automobile license plate. If one of y'all finds it, do not touch it! Hold up your hands." Hightower grinned. "I'm sure y'all have done that before. Hold up your hands and holler for me." He instructed the sheriff to have his prisoners fan out from the road edge into the pasture. The men walked into the field, and not five minutes later, one of the prisoners raised his hands and shouted, "Yeah, license plate here, boss!"

Hightower noted it was where Truett said, "Slung it into that field next to where we were parked."

The plate lay face down half covered in mud, weathered with rust, but still plenty readable. Hightower pried it loose from the dried mud and rubbed the crusty dirt several times with his hand. The missing license plate had been found. "Lieutenant, I think you're gonna be a believer before this is all over. Boy was here. Show me where the patrol car was parked."

Stanley pointed without hesitation. "Across the road, over in that little clearing between them trees."

Hightower pointed across the road where Stanley indicated. "Sheriff, have your men walk through those woods there. See if they can find a ring of car keys, will you? Lieutenant, let's you and me head down to where y'all found the bodies."

Without objection, Count allowed the agents to walk from the pasture back onto his road. "Being here only that one night, pitch black dark, now a year later, Truett sure remembers this place. He described this road with such detail that I'll bet I can show you where they were."

The frisky Weimaraner followed as the two agents kept walking until they reached the hilltop. Hightower surveyed its opposite side. "The officers came from this direction. Truett said he could tell a car was coming by its headlight beams."

"Wasn't no secret which way they came."

The two lawmen crossed over the hilltop and continued down Arc Road's long, gradual slope. "Y'all know about a car going backwards to that driveway down the hill? Truett tried to get away in his Chevy Impala convertible. They chased him down and blocked him in."

"Yeah, we know a car chase occurred back down that hill. Old folks living there told us what they seen. No secret about that either. Didn't know what kind of car it was, though."

"Okay, so far he's right in step with what y'all knew. Evans and Williams drove off over this hill with the officers in the Oldsmobile. Truett stayed behind to back the patrol car into that little clearing where you found it."

The two agents walked halfway down the hill. Thick woods lining the narrow dirt road shaded the morning sun. "A few minutes later Truett got to about this area when he heard rapid gunfire."

Hightower and Stanley continued down the hill until reaching the point where the road bottomed out to a flat grade. The men stood quietly in the road and looked around. They had arrived at their destination, the murder scene.

Count walked several yards into the woods. Under the thick canopy he zigzagged, sniffing the dirt, until finally standing where the three officers' bodies were found, the patch of woods where their blood pooled onto the straw-covered ground. Count bowed and then sounded a soft, mournful moan.

"I don't blame you, big fella," Stanley told the dog. "I feel the same way."

Hightower tilted his head and looked through the trees. "Something tells me they didn't just sit here in these woods like targets in a gallery. Nobody would have. Had to be more to it than that."

"You think? Hell, Bob! They was all handcuffed together."

"I don't care if they were all balled and chained."

"You think they'd'a kicked and screamed, huh?"

"I would've! You would've. No, must've been some words got said that made somebody hit the kill switch. I can't find a cause in it, but I'm thinking it was probably Evans. Something about his behavior, the way he acted after the crime, seemed too damn cool, in a cold-blooded way. Makes no sense. I wish Truett had seen what happened, but he didn't, or else he would've told me. No, something or more likely someone pissed somebody off that started all the gun play. It is possible this whole thing could've just been in the cards, you know, God's will, if you're a religious man."

"God's will? Shit! Sometimes I wonder about you, Hightower."

Hightower grinned. "That's okay Lieutenant. Sometimes I wonder about me, too."

"Was over a damn stolen car! Makes no difference, wouldn't of changed nothing. They'd have still ended up dead. Them bastards had no conscience when it came to killing. To me it don't matter who or what started it. I don't care. Only thing I care about is seeing those goddamn sons of bitches fry."

"If Mr. Merritt can get Truett to testify, I'm pretty sure you'll get your wish."

"He's gonna need more than that little punk's confession."

"Well, I'm with you there, and that's why we're here."

The lead agent walked a twenty-foot circle in the road from one side to the other, ditch to ditch. Just beyond the left ditch an old oak hovered over the dirt, its branches stretched beyond the narrow road. A few yards behind the massive trunk a wooden one-room field house leaned twisted. Its rotted walls barely stood; its roof had collapsed.

"Jim, right here is where all hell broke."

"Yeah, I remember." Stanley gazed through the surrounding woods and took in a deep breath. "I remember." After a short pause, he recalled, "Over yonder a ways is where we found Mr. Gravitt's wallet. Had more than one hundred dollars in it. Probably slung it out before he was killed. I figured he wasn't gonna let the bastards have it."

Hightower scratched a one-foot X in the dirt with the toe of his boot. "Right here under this oak's branches is where the Oldsmobile was parked."

"Nope, the Oldsmobile was parked down there about a hundred feet or so." Stanley pointed. "See how the road bends down there? See that little group of trees on the right? Was wedged in between them trees. Look at this picture. What's that look like to you? Looks like an Old-smobile, don't it? I know exactly where it was, and it sure wasn't here like you say."

"I understand that's where you found it, but when Truett drove down here, the Oldsmobile was under this oak tree." Hightower explained, "He parked his Chevy, got out, and walked through this ditch up this bank. He froze when he saw Evans and Williams standing about where that dog is. Saw the officers lying on the ground and then heard a gurgling sound coming from one of them. Said it reminded him of when he was a little boy watching his daddy slaughter a hog. Split its face open with an axe. The animal gurgled as its last breath blew through the blood."

From the crime scene photos Hightower picked out a close-up picture of Officer Everett's gun belt. "You see these two empty bullet loops on the back of his belt?"

"Sure, saw it that morning."

"Did you wonder why they were empty?"

"Didn't give it much thought at the time."

"Williams took 'em. Truett saw Evans hand Williams a gun then he shined his flashlight on Everett's belt. Williams took the two bullets, loaded the gun, leaned over one of the officers, and shot him point blank in the face. Truett said the gurgling sound stopped after Williams fired the rounds."

Stanley raged, "The gurgling stopped! He waited a year to say the gurgling stopped? Son-of-a-bitch! I'll be goddamned if that little bastard gets immunity with me. I'll split his face open with an axe. For once I'll use this damn badge to my liking."

"If you don't mind, are you quite finished? Thank you." Hightower, ever the unswerving lawman, shook his head. "And sometimes you wonder about me, huh?"

"You weren't here to see it. Hell, I could smell it. I put my hands in it. Got blood all over me from carrying them boys out of here."

"I know."

"Oh, you do?" The scruffy agent continued. "You don't know shit, Hightower. You uppity-ass boys from your damned marble tower in Milledgeville. Yeah, that's right. 'I know' is easy for you to say, but let me tell you something right now; I guar-an-tee I'll die before ever seeing anything like that again. Least I hope so."

"I hope so too, Lieutenant, for both our sakes." Hightower slapped Stanley on the shoulder. "Kind of taints this glamorous profession of ours, don't it?"

Stanley softly growled, "You got that right."

"I'd like your thoughts on this, more out of curiosity than anything else. One of the guns had only two empty cartridges in it. That makes sense from this picture and Truett's story. What doesn't make sense is Officer Davis' autopsy showed he was shot at least five times in the face at close range. Truett said Williams fired the gun two times, not five. Seems to me as vivid as he recalled that night, he'd know the difference."

"Davis was already dead. They were all dead. Didn't Truett say he heard gunfire on his way down here? Didn't he say they were already lying on the ground when first he seen 'em? Obviously they'd been shot before he ever got down here. Either it was Williams or Evans, one or both, who'd already shot Davis three times. Those two rounds Williams fired makes five. What's so hard to understand about that?"

"I'm assuming the officers carried their guns fully loaded."

"I think that'd be an accurate assumption."

"When the guns were found, one held six empty cartridges, another had five empty and a loaded misfire, and the third held only those two empty casings and four empty chambers. From your report, no bullet casings were found." Hightower looked at Stanley. "Is that right?"

"No, not no thirty-eights."

"Okay, if indeed they carried their guns fully loaded, nineteen shots in all were fired, six, six, five, and two. Doctor Howard's autopsies back that up. So the question is what happened to the third gun's first six spent rounds?"

"I don't know. Does it matter?"

"Here's what I think. Evans handed Williams an empty gun. I find that very interesting, Lieutenant. Don't you?"

"Not really, but I'm sure you're gonna tell me why that's so interesting."

"I believe you didn't find those empty casings because they were in Evans' pocket. I'm trying to understand exactly what took place here. That may be impossible, but at the very least I want to prove our boy is telling the truth. So far I can't place a lie in any of what he's said. Not here on this dirt bank...and not on the other side of that hill, either." Hightower squatted down, peered from side to side in the dirt. He stood to think a moment before looking closer. "I'll be damned! A year later, and still here."

"What's still here?"

Hightower pointed at the dirt. "Take a good look at this, these ruts here. You can easily make 'em out. They're from Truett's Chevrolet."

"Truett's Chevrolet?"

"Yes! Truett told me on the way to Atlanta he slid his Chevy off the road hereabouts." Hightower pointed to more ruts in the road. "And here!" He closely followed the still visible ruts across the road. "Look here, this imprint." The two agents squatted down in the right side ditch. "Evans and Williams had to jack up the Chevy to push it clear. This imprint is from the bumper jack's base plate. Amazing! It's all still here." Hightower looked at Stanley. "It all fits, just as he described. Boys got a fine memory; I'll give him that. He's gonna make an excellent witness for Mr. Merritt."

"I hope you're right." Stanley continued looking at the marks in the road.

"Oh I think so. Of course I do have two big concerns: Evans and Williams."

"Yeah, what about 'em?"

"We've got Truett's story: the events on this road, the patrol car, missing license plate, the pasture, bullets, guns, and so on. That's hard stuff. But how are we going to prove what he's saying about the other two and their involvement?"

"His confession. It's called direct evidence, Hightower. Corroborated!"

"Yeah, maybe to us it is, but you think to a jury? I'm sure Williams will be easy enough. Merritt's got no problem with that connection. Partnership, motive, and as you mentioned, corroborating witnesses. But Evans? How are you going to fit him in? On Truett's word alone? No, I think not. But then again, maybe so."

"Huh? Double talk. I don't get it."

"One thing stands out in my mind. Truett told me Evans seemed to know the officers really well. Said Evans talked to them using their first names and they did the same to him."

"So?"

"Evans has said many times, even told Hutchins and Ragsdale, he knew those officers real well. In fact, said they were his good friends. Said, families too!"

"Where are you going with all this?"

"Don't you see? Truett told me he'd never met Evans before that night. Didn't know him! And I'm sure when it comes time, Evans will say he doesn't know any Wade Truett and probably say the same about Venson Williams."

"I don't follow you."

Hightower stared at Lieutenant Stanley in wonderment. "Sure you do. If Truett didn't know Alex Evans before that night, then how would he know about Evans' close first-name friendship with the officers? He wouldn't. Not unless he and they were all right here together that night. How else did Truett make that connection if he didn't hear it firsthand? No other way, right?" Hightower stared at Stanley. "Right?"

"Okay, you've convinced me that Truett was here, but it's gonna take more than what you're saying to convince me he didn't do any of the shooting."

"I might not be good at convincing you, but when I look into a man's eyes, I can tell whether he's being truthful or not. That's a fact."

"Oh it is, is it?" Stanley chuckled. "If you say so. Now if those lie-detector eyes of yours can see we're all finished here, let's get ourselves up and gone. I'm hungry. Didn't have no breakfast this morning, thanks to you."

Hightower and Stanley began the one-mile walk back up, over, and down Arc Road's long dirt hill. Count, side-stepping in the road, sniffed the dirt as he led their way.

Stanley noted, "Sure looks to me like Evans and that big mouth just might put his own sorry ass in the hot seat."

"Fifty thousand volts worth."

"And you wanna know something else, Hightower? One of these days you just might make a decent investigator."

"One of these days you just might be right, Lieutenant."

Count, having finished escort duty, trotted back down his gravel driveway as the agents continued their walk.

The sheriff stood in the road and reported, "Sorry, boys, didn't find any car keys."

Hightower gave the man an appreciative smile. "Didn't think you would, but thanks for looking."

After almost three hours, the agents finally arrived back to where their Arc Road journey began.

Hightower got in his car and left, but Stanley, before leaving, had one last look down Arc Road's rutted course. He took in a deep breath and then blew out his only feeling. "Goddamn this road."

After driving away, neither lawman would ever return to Gwinnett's infamous two-mile stretch of red Georgia dirt.

Twenty-four hours later, Hightower felt his way through the murky mud bottom of Black Creek. Bigger than its designation, the creek was an inky-brackish river flowing southeasterly through Prestwood Lake. The lake bordered the north side of Hartsville, South Carolina, Truett's hometown. Two bridges spanned the river, north and south. The dark brackish waters made a perfect hideaway for the clothes worn on Arc Road and the Chevy Impala's crime scene tires. Truett had told Hightower that he used the bridges as a platform to fling his and Williams clothes and shoes worn on Arc Road and the getaway car's tires into the river. Two Georgia State Troopers anchored a rope tethered to the former Navy frogman as he felt his way, blindly searching along the river bottom.

After a half-hour search, Hightower drug two of the four tires out of the river and up the weed-choked bank.

The slightly worn tires fit Truett's description, same size and make. No clothes were found in the river, but with the matching tires, Hightower gained even more belief in Truett's story. Although not necessarily a case clincher, the evidence added up nicely enough that the GBI agent felt his pursuit of the electric chair for Evans and Williams was justified.

∽

During the summer of 1965 Reid Merritt directed a daily routine of interrogators shooting rapid-firing questions at Truett. They paused long enough for him to only partially answer before moving on. The approach would ensure that if Truett was to be the young solicitor's prize witness, there had to be no doubt his star boy could prevail. Truett's convincing answers throughout the four-month-long repetitious interrogation came forthright without hesitation, each and every time, never swaying from the original confession.

In early July, Solicitor Merritt believed he had enough proof to charge Alex Evans, Wade Truett, and Venson Williams with first-degree murder for the role they played in causing the deaths of Gwinnett County Police officers Jerry Everett, Ralph Davis, and Jesse Gravitt. The three murders occurred during the conspired theft of an automobile shortly after midnight April 17, 1964 on a quiet dirt road near the small town of Duluth, Georgia.

Addressing Gwinnett's grand jury, Merritt requested criminal indictments be brought against the three suspects. The solicitor provided evidence that showed a motive for the conspiracy along with a full list of witnesses he planned to introduce should the jury allow the State to move forward with a prosecution. He added that Wade

Truett, a defendant himself who conspired in the theft of the automobile but did not participate in the actual murders, would be offered immunity for his testimony against the actual killers, Evans and Williams. Immunity was offered because without Truett's testimony, the evidence alone, all circumstantial, would not be sufficient for the State to secure murder convictions against his two partners.

Merritt further explained, "the many witnesses he intended to put on the stand could testify only to parts of Truett's confession, but combining their testimony would indeed corroborate the timeline of events Truett claimed, thus giving him credibility." Merritt added that if the defendants were found guilty it would also serve to debunk future accusations in the Court of Appeals that the State itself had rigged the trial by scheming with Truett and those many witnesses to achieve that result.

Merritt continued his address to the grand jury stating that aside from Truett's damning testimony, he foresaw Evans exercising his right granted under Georgia law to give an unsworn statement from the witness stand. That law allows a defendant to speak on his own behalf directly to the jury while absent of any examination by counsel or penalty of perjury.

"I expect Mr. Evans will, using the law to his advantage, attempt to sway the jury by espousing those most absurd claims and accusations encompassed in an alibi of which he has already made public. I believe, in part, those claims to include 'this crime was a conspiracy on the highest order perpetrated not by me but by county crime bosses ruling over county citizens et al., who comprised an organized crime syndicate that in the end killed those officers for what they knew.' These claims by Mr. Evans of pervasive guilt and premeditated murder would bring to light names of upstanding men and women in Gwinnett who, organized or otherwise, had no involvement in this crime. The State, in its exhaustive investigation of these murders, has found no specific or indirect connection germane to Mr. Evans' accusations. It is for this reason that the State has no intention of calling them to the stand, which thereby would allow the defendant a ploy attempt to slander their good names."

Merritt offered, "The State will subpoena and have waiting, in the event it's necessary, several current and past law enforcement officers as character witnesses. In particular former law enforcement partners of Mr. Evans who will testify to his explosive temper and acts of abuse committed against private citizens while in his official capacity as a Gwinnett County sheriff deputy. This most abhorrent conduct, which became a standard practice by Deputy Evans, would eventually lead to his dismissal from law enforcement."

To support Merritt's accusations, grand jury members heard brief statements from GBI agents Hightower and Stanley, as well as DeKalb detectives Homer Lee Cheek and John Crunkleton. Following a one-and-a-half-hour presentation, the grand jury agreed with the solicitor. Criminal indictments were brought against the three conspirators, charging them with first-degree murder. U.S. Marshals took custody of Alex Evans at the Federal Prison in Milan, Michigan, where he had been transferred to finish his two-year stretch for manufacturing illegal liquor. He was served with a warrant for his arrest and immediately brought to Atlanta for confinement.

Marshals served Venson Williams with his arrest warrant inside the Atlanta Federal Penitentiary where he would remain until his arraignment. Wade Truett, having already been transferred from the Federal Correctional

Institute in Tallahassee, Florida, was confined in Atlanta, bouncing back and forth from the Fulton County Jail to the Gwinnett County Jail while investigators continued their interrogation. Although he was now under arrest for the murders but promised immunity for his testimony against Evans and Williams, official consideration could be agreed to only by the trial judge.

Toward the end of the first week in July, fourteen months after the murders, news broke of the indictments. Newspaper headlines in bold lettering read Grand Jury Indicts Three Men in Triple Police Slaying.

For more than a year the press had slung an ocean of ink at Georgia's number-one news story. Recurring front-page pictures of the slain officers lying in the woods were now mercifully replaced with prison mugshots of Evans, Williams, and Truett.

To those who lost faith in law enforcement, the wheels of justice were finally rolling. The welcomed news of indictments could not have come a moment sooner, for as unbearably sad as the story had begun, the end would be that much more heartening. To the families it would be a soothing comfort; to the law-abiding soul, peace of mind. Folks formerly dismayed by a constant stream of nothing-new editorials eagerly sought every special edition. Again, tireless paperboys feasted on the nickels paid by dedicated scrapbookers up and down Georgia's countless dirt roads.

THE TRIAL

After announcing the indictments, Governor Carl Sanders, with Solicitor Reid Merritt standing at his side, gave a televised press conference declaring, "The killers have been found." He commended GBI agents for their determined efforts in solving the most heinous crime in Georgia's history. Newspapers statewide plastered their front pages with Police Murder Case Solved!

Criminal defense attorney James Dorsey, representing Venson Williams in the first of the co-trials, cried "Foul." Dorsey, a highly experienced, well-regarded trial lawyer and former leader of Georgia's Republican Party, had at one time himself been a celebrated prosecutor for the State. Robert Thompson, defending Alex Evans in his trial, decried, "What Dorsey Said." A dedicated defense attorney, Thompson, who based his practice in Buford, had become one of Georgia's staunchest advocates for criminal rights. On various occasions, for a variety of reasons, he represented several of the players that law enforcement had interrogated during its investigation of the crime. In fact several of his former clients were under subpoena to appear as witnesses for the prosecution in the two murder trials.

From the start both defense attorneys came out swinging—or more accurately, objecting—with strong condemnation in reference to the public statements made by Governor Sanders and Solicitor Merritt.

The Honorable Charles Pittard would preside over both trials held in the Superior Court of Gwinnett County. Judge Pittard stood as a fair, impartial, black-robed, gavel-pounding jurist if ever there was one. At the pretrial conference, Dorsey addressed Judge Pittard. "Your Honor, if I may, the governor's statement and consequent media publications have so tainted the neutrality of potential jurors as to have effectively now left only a predetermined verdict of guilty before trial deliberations are underway. This is the most grievous indignation ever to assault the model of justice. Therefore, if the Court may allow, the moving party files a pretrial motion, and Counsel feels the Court obligated, to a change of venue as far from Gwinnett County as possible under these circumstances."

Knowing full well the media sensationalism the two trials would acquire, Judge Pittard's pretrial diligence would test the depth of his court-ruling knowledge, one that the man of granite could endure no matter what size the hammer or chisel. He countered any pretrial jockeying from defense motions with stern advice to avoid the slightest suggestion of post-trial appeals. With a conspirator turning state's witness, the defense knew it had an uphill battle. Its strategy would more than likely be built on an expectation of conviction and appeals built around opinionated court and trial improprieties. Judge

Pittard was a master at planning for and thwarting such situations.

Pittard gave notice that a difference of opinion for any court decision or jury verdict in his trials would likely be neither advantageous nor successful. He set a precedent regarding how he would conduct the trials when Dorsey filed the motion for a change in venue. "Mr. Dorsey," the judge said, "you will have an opportunity to query each prospective juror as to whether the governor's statement and subsequent media publications have caused an opinion prior to proceedings that may be detrimental to the outcome desired by the defendant, but I feel certain your question in this regard will be without impact, as there is no place in Georgia that this crime has gone unheard. Motion denied."

Each attorney was highly admired for his noble resolve, but united, Dorsey and Thompson formed a defense team plenty capable of succeeding in a verdict of not guilty, even against the accusers' overwhelming odds. After all, the State had in Reid Merritt a young county solicitor who had never prosecuted a murder case. If Merritt was to lead the State to prosecutorial victory, he would need the help of another learned jurist, Luther C. Hames, an exceptional prosecutor who at the time was solicitor general of Cobb County. Hames, a fervent believer in the Ten Commandments, held an intense disgust for murder. Those three killings in particular caused his wrath to soar. From his early teens, Luther had dreamed and prepared for a moment such as this to present itself. Without hesitation he gladly accepted the State's request to assist Merritt.

The two defendants were to be tried separately for the murder of Jerry Everett. If a jury convicted the two killers in the first trials, the State would sentence them to the electric chair, provided the verdict was brought without recommendation for leniency. That was the law in Georgia. Without recommendation, a judge had no choice but to impose the death sentence. The convicted got the chair. However, if the jury found each defendant not guilty or guilty with a recommendation for leniency, Merritt had potentially two more charges for the murders of Davis and Gravitt to get what he and the good folks of Gwinnett County wanted. Not to mention what Hightower, Stanley and a full assortment of Georgia's finest wanted: a swift finality of justice.

As trial dates approached, advocates for the slain police officers impatiently counted down the days. Folks in Gwinnett knew the event was going to be Georgia's greatest courtroom spectacle, and they wanted in. In spite of their presumptions, though, only one thing was certain. The gathering storm of national media meant the eyes of a nation, many millions, for sure, would be watching. It had been eighteen agonizing months since the world heard the horrifying news about three police officers handcuffed and slaughtered in the woods of a rural North Georgia town. The trials were soon to be the second round of global attention to fall on the county, and residents hoped this round would avenge the first.

On Tuesday, October 5, 1965, county police set up road blocks at 7:30 AM, stopping all traffic from entering downtown Lawrenceville's central square. As a warm autumn sunrise thawed the cool morning mist, a large assembly of well-dressed spectators gathered around Gwinnett's old brick courthouse, its grand façade cornerstone having been placed more than one hundred years before. A four-faced clock tower rose in supreme dignity, reaching twice higher than the two-story justice hall it adjoined.

Already inside behind the defendants' table sat Venson Williams, pale, thin, and dressed in a loosely fitted dark suit. Before sun-up under tight security a dozen U.S. Marshals driving unmarked cars had convoyed him from the Atlanta Federal Penitentiary to the courthouse where they quietly whisked him through a back entrance off the town square. To Williams' right sat defense attorney James Dorsey.

During the morning hours closed court proceedings finalized the jury selection. In both trials the jury would consist of a twelve-member group with two alternates.

At one o'clock, following lunch recess, Judge Pittard ordered, "Guards, will you please open the courthouse doors and allow the people to enter peacefully."

Within minutes a scrunched-together line of one hundred fifty eager spectators made their way up the wooden staircase leading into the second-floor courtroom. A handful of news reporters were allowed to observe and take notes, but no cameras or tape recorders were permitted.

When all general seats were filled, the remaining folks tried to create their own standing-room section. Judge Pittard did not oblige their effort. He stated, "The court hated to make this announcement, but prior to this trial's beginning it was announced that there would be no standing in the courtroom unless it was by officers. As long as there are seats available, it is open for spectators, but we cannot allow people standing."

As the shuffling of feet and squirming of bodies quieted, Judge Pittard spoke out. "All right, guards, please close and secure the doors. I believe there are several members of the Davis, Everett, and Gravitt families waiting in my chambers. Please escort them into the courtroom and seat them in the front pews provided."

The families were brought into the courtroom. Spectators and court officials observed a solemn moment of respect as they entered. Members of each family attended every day for both trials for Everett's murder. After the jury was seated, Judge Pittard struck his gavel three times on a wood block atop his bench. "We will be in order now."

His consideration centered upon the twelve men sitting adjacent to him. He addressed them for the first time the same as he would throughout both trials, "Gentlemen of the jury." Pittard explained the court's responsibility followed by the jury's civic obligation. "While this case is on trial and while evidence, arguments, and the charge of the court are being introduced to you, it is going to be necessary that you be kept together throughout the trial. The court has made arrangements for your quarters in the apartments down at the bus station. Meals will be served you at the bus station, and you will, at all times, be under the care of the bailiffs. I know it is going to be a hardship on some of you who serve as jurors, but that is necessary matter. The court will undertake to make your service as easy as possible. Should any of you wish to get messages to your family or need any clothes or shaving arrangements, if you will let the bailiff know your needs, the court will see that they are secured for you. I have stated to the court, we will have at least one recess in the morning and one in the afternoon, and during the trial of the case, any juror that feels any necessity or urge for a recess, if you will call that to the court's attention, I will arrange it for you."

Finally he ordered his stern instructions about any Court recess: "You are not allowed to read any newspaper accounts of this trial while it is in session; you are not allowed to hear any radio broadcast or television broadcast of any of the events of the trial while it is in session. You should not even discuss this case among yourselves until you have heard all of the evidence, arguments of counsel, and charge of the court and retired to your jury room to begin your deliberations. Certainly it cannot be discussed by you with any other person or should not even be discussed in your presence. Of course the bailiffs will be with you at all times to see that these rules are carried out."

❧

Meanwhile, a Deep South spectacle unfolded on the courthouse lawn where only small patches of uninhabited ground remained. Grand hardwoods, stretched close together, shaded the entire courthouse square. Hundreds, if not more, from all points, county and state, patiently waited for news relayed from the proceedings inside. Many sat in folding chairs or on rolled-out blankets; most stood, chatting in small groups, or strolled about looking to reconnect with lost ties. Late arrivals watched from all sidewalks boxing the square. Strangers swapped kind memories of the murdered officers and harsh methods of punishment if the accused were found guilty. Unwieldy television cameras bobbled throughout the grounds as spiffy-suited reporters extended microphones to blushing Southern starlets. The grand affair continued beyond the shaded square, spilling along Clayton Street and farther into its alleys. Truck farmers parked beside the courthouse lawn sold iced-down watermelons cut into quarters. Street vendors sold select tomatoes and onions sliced thick for sandwich lunches. Farm boys clad in tattered coveralls scooped boiled peanuts straight out of scalding hot pots. Full bags quickly sold before cooling. Vendors' little brothers roamed the lawn peddling small bags of roasted peanuts for a dime. Bright red coolers packed to the brim with Atlanta's thirst quencher, six-and-a-half-ounce bottled Coca Cola, appeared under shady store-front awnings.

Many more uniformed lawmen than folks had ever seen at one time, state troopers, sheriff deputies, and county policemen, surrounded the courthouse to ensure peace and order. Several FBI agents walked amid the crowd. Rumor had it that in the grass stalked a vigilante, a killer's assassin. For certain there was no shortage of people who had the desire for revenge.

℀

Before the first witness was sworn in, Judge Pittard felt the heat, literally. An early October blast of mid-August warmth suffocated the enclosed courtroom. Pittard addressed the jury. "Gentlemen, would you like some windows raised? It's too hot. Bailiffs, please raise some of the windows." A wave of cool air rolled into the justice hall. After waiting, he nodded. "Mr. Merritt, you may proceed by calling your first witness." With those words the murder trial for Officer Jerry Everett finally began.

The prosecution sequenced those subpoenaed to lay a foundation for the state's most important witness, Wade Truett.

First called to the stand was Lawrence Hartmann, owner of the burned Oldsmobile found on Arc Road. Before entering the witness box, Hartmann, like every state's witness to follow in both trials, placed one hand on the Bible and raised his other. "I swear that the evidence I give shall be the truth, the whole truth, and nothing but the truth, so help me God." In the Bible Belt, reciting those words caused Southerners to look upward.

Hartmann testified that he owned a 1963 Oldsmobile two-door coupe. On the morning of April 17, 1964, he reported the car missing from his apartment parking lot where he'd left it the night before. Three days later, after seeing the car in a Lawrenceville impound yard, Hartmann could not positively identify the charred remains as once belonging to him.

After dismissing his first witness, Merritt called Clyde Pruitt, the radio operator for Gwinnett County police. Pruitt testified that he dispatched officers Everett and Davis to Arc Road following A. C. Mills' telephone complaint about cars going up and down his road at one thirty in the morning.

Third to appear on the stand was Ruby Mills. Her husband, A. C., was unable to attend court because of his failing health. Ruby Mills told the court what she recalled, or more accurately what she didn't recall.

The state's witnesses kept coming, nineteen in all. Officer Ray Sexton told of the ghastly scene he found in the woods of Arc Road that Friday morning. GBI agent M. J. Vandiver testified to collecting the officers' guns Bobby Tidwell found along Beaver Ruin Road that Sunday afternoon. A thirty-minute recess followed the morning testimonies.

When court reconvened, GBI Lieutenant James Stanley took the stand. Stanley had conducted the crime scene investigation. For the remainder of day one Stanley was questioned first in direct from Hames then in cross by Thompson. The lieutenant stated, in part:

Q: What is your name, please?

A: James H. Stanley.

Q: I ask you if you have had an occasion or if you did have the occasion in 1964 and in April of that year to come to Gwinnett County as an investigative officer of the GBI.

A: Yes, sir, I did. I investigated the crime scene, morning that the officers were found on Arc Road.

Q: What time did you arrive, Mr. Stanley?

A: It was approximately eleven o'clock, I believe.

Q: What, if anything, did you find when you arrived there?

A: We found… observed the location of the Gwinnett County police car, the officers' bodies, and also an Oldsmobile was burning at the scene.

Q: What, if anything, did you observe about the bodies of the officers?

A: During examination of the bodies I found that the three officers were handcuffed together.

Q: Now, I hand you here State's Exhibit Number twenty-two and ask you if you can identify these.

A: Yes, sir, these are the two pairs of handcuffs which were used to handcuff the three officers together.

Q: Now, would you come down here and show or demonstrate to the jury how these were on the bodies of the officers, using Mr. Rusk, Mr. Hightower, and myself?

A: Yes, sir.

Judge Pittard expressed his concern. "You have a key for them?"

Mr. Hames: "Yes, sir, I hope he does."

Stanley's straight-faced expression softened to a modest smile. "Yes, sir, I do have the key."

A faint mix of laughter and whispers filtered through the quiet courtroom. The nearly inaudible disturbance raised the judge's ire. "This trial is not being conducted for any exhibition, and the court cannot tolerate any show of emotion from the audience whatsoever. Now, proceed, Mr. Hames."

"Thank you, Your Honor." He proceeded to cuff one of the men by the right hand as Officer Jesse Gravitt. He cuffed another man's left hand by the same pair of cuffs as

Officer Ralph Davis. Finally, he connected the right hand of the third man to the chain of the first two as Officer Jerry Everett. Once the jury had gotten a good look at how they were connected, Mr. Hames said, "All right, Mr. Stanley, you had better unlock them. Go back to the stand, please sir."

Q: Who removed the cuffs from the bodies of the officers?

A: I did.

Mr. Hames: "Your Honor, I have no further questions for this witness. He belongs to you, Mr. Thompson."

Mr. Thompson: "We have nothing further of the witness, your Honor."

The Court: "All right, you may go down, Mr. Stanley."

As Stanley's testimony came to an end so did the first day of proceedings.

Judge Pittard again expressed his stern orders to the jury to refrain from related conversation. "Gentlemen, I think we will recess here. We will remain in order. Gentlemen of the jury, as I expressed to you this morning, you are going to have to remain together while the trial is in session." He reiterated his earlier warnings about not discussing the case or otherwise learning about the case, and added, "You may, if you wish, play card games, bridge, rook or something, in your spare time. Weather permits and you wish to walk or take exercise under the presence of the bailiffs, that is in order, but the law requires that you remain together and that you have no contact whatever with anything outside of the trial of this case."

Although Lieutenant Stanley's testimony described the murder scene, trial day one offered little new to courtroom spectators already knowledgeable from the published facts. Day two differed with the graphic testimony of Dr. Larry Howard. Solicitor Hames began his direct examination by first establishing the doctor's credentials. As Dr. Howard described the morbid details of Officer Everett's autopsy, all in the courtroom listened intently while coldly staring in contempt at the motionless defendant, Venson Williams.

Here in part is the doctor's testimony:

Q: What is your name, please?

A: Doctor Larry Howard.

Q: By whom are you employed?

A: The Crime Laboratory in the State of Georgia.

Q: Where did you get your formal training?

A: Bachelor's degree, University of Minnesota, and post doctors training, Emory University, nineteen fifty-six to nineteen fifty-seven.

Q: Doctor, I will ask you did you have the occasion to come to Gwinnett County on or about the seventeenth day of April nineteen sixty-four?

A: Yes, I did. I went to Arc Road in Gwinnett County and viewed three bodies that were found there.

Q: Would you give to the court and jury a description of what you found when you arrived there?

A: Three police officers lying on the ground handcuffed together, and of course the bodies were bloodstained, and there was blood on the ground, and it was apparent from the examination at the scene at that point that they had been shot.

Q: What was the condition of these three men as to whether they were dead or alive?

A: They had all died as a result of multiple bullet wounds.

Q: Did you examine the body of Officer Jerry R. Everett?

A: I did. Yes, sir.

Q: Would you give to the court and jury the results of your examination of that body?

A: This officer showed many bullet wounds. The first wound I observed and examined was an entrance wound in the back of the right leg and exit wound in front of the right leg. The bloody drainage, or blood drainage, from the wound was both toward the crotch and down toward the knee, and most of the drainage came from the exit wound. Vertical drainage going down toward the knee showed the wound was received sometime before death and showed that the officer stood some time prior to death.

Q: Based on your examination and the amount of blood, the distance that the blood had traveled down the leg, do you have an opinion as to how long he remained standing after he received that particular wound?

A: I can't say exactly, but it wasn't very long. In a period of less than an hour, certainly, between the time he received the wound and the time he met his death, and this wound was not responsible for death; it was a non-fatal wound.

Q: What other wounds did you find on his body?

A: Also a bullet wound in the right shoulder that caught the body in a slightly upward direction and pierced both pleural cavities, and about two-hundred cc's of blood in the right pleural cavity, the cavity that holds the right lung. The right lung, however, was not collapsed, which indicated this wound was received very shortly prior to his death.

Q: Did you make any examination of any other wound on his person?

A: Yes, sir, there were several wounds in his head of which there was powder tattooing around. One of the wounds went in behind the right ear and the bullet lodged over the left temple, part coming out, I believe through the left cheekbone. And also an apparent double wound entry in the back of the head. Altogether three bullets were recovered from the head area.

Q: Did you make any determination as to the distance of these wounds that was produced by the gun?

A: I examined the distribution of what we call powder tattoo around and made an infrared photograph, and the relative distribution would be consistent with one- to two-feet muzzle target distance.

Q: Now, when you spoke of powder deposits, what is the significance of that, Doctor?

A: This indicates that the muzzles of the target distance, in this case the head, was within a range of two feet or so, and this is also true of the wound in the leg, but not true of the wound in the shoulder. No powder residue was around the wound in the right shoulder that I could detect.

Q: Your testimony then would have what effect, Doctor, as to what distance the gun was from?

A: Approximately two feet, whereas the wound in the shoulder, probably be three feet or greater from the body of the officer at the time it was discharged.

At this point in the testimony, Hames demanded a more graphic explanation than Doctor Howard's mere words described. He intended to humanize the carnage so the court and jury further comprehended the atrocity.

Q: Would you come down and use my body as an illustration of the wounds of various points of entry you discovered?

A: Yes.

He stood up from the stand and stepped over to Mr. Hames. Dr. Howard continued:

"One point of entry was directly in back of the head here, and this appeared to be a double wound. Another point of entry was here, with the touching of the ear, and going in behind the ear and lodging over here in the right temple area. In other words, the bullet track went forward and upward slightly. Another wound was in the right shoulder with the bullet entering here and going across the top of the right lung and lodging in this part of the body. The other wound was just below the buttocks on the crease of the trousers and went through the medial, outer aspect of the leg and out the front. There was powder residue around that also."

Dr. Howard speculated that Officer Everett's right leg wound could have occurred while he tried to run away. He also speculated that they had possibly been shot while standing up and collapsed on the ground. To prosecute these murders the State had no obligation or reason to establish how the mechanics of the execution occurred, only that it did and resulted in three dead Gwinnett County police officers stretched on the ground in a desolate patch of woods. Howard did not testify to the mutilated bullet found in the back of Everett's neck. This noteworthy bullet was found by mortician Ryman Pendley while preparing the officer's body for his casket. Dr. Howard logged the bullet in his final report, but given that he did not find or remove it during the autopsy, Howard made no mention of it during the trial.

Q: Doctor, in all, from your examination, how many bullet pellets were fired into the body?

A: Approximately five; at least five, I should say.

Q: Was there any difficulty in tracing the number of points of entry?

A: In the head there was, because the damage was so extensive to the skull and one of the bullets shattered, broke into two pieces and caused two exit wounds, so I can't be sure how many wounds were in the head. When I took the skull cap off, one of the bullets fell out of the officer's skull, and I didn't know the point of lodging. There were numerous bullet tracks throughout the brain. Death would be very rapid under these conditions.

Q: You say you recovered certain bullet pellets or objects from the brain?

A: Yes, sir, and also from the left chest.

Q: Doctor, what was the condition of the officer's hands when you arrived there at the scene?

A: They were handcuffed together.

Q: Were the handcuffs disengaged in your presence?

A: Yes, sir.

Mr. Hames: Thank you, sir. Your Honor, I have no more questions.

Defense counsel stood and addressed the court. "We have no questions for this witness."

Judge Pittard turned and said, "Dr. Howard, you may come down."

As Dr. Howard stepped down from the witness stand, the faces inside the courtroom looked stunned. Howard's testimony had defined brutality people had not previously heard. Allowing court and spectators a calming moment, Judge Pittard announced, "We will take a short recess at this time. Gentlemen of the jury, you may retire to your jury room for water or Coca-Cola and have a cigarette, if you wish. We will recess until two forty-five."

Time-consuming procedural bickering between attorneys brought an early end to the trial's second day.

Courthouse and grounds cleared, Lawrenceville's square resumed its amber-lit serenity. Restless news reporters gnawed unfiltered cigarettes while talking to their editors from public telephones. All four phones inside the square were in use long after dark. Handwritten notes read aloud from inside the glass telephone booths transformed pencil scribble into lengthy narratives of gruesome testimony. Late editions printed out Georgia Police Murder Trial Day Two Ends, a luring headline to readers eager for all the latest.

Trial day three would prove by far the most drama filled and certainly replete with disruptions of argument and objection compared to the smooth, orderly proceedings of days one and two. For all of day three, court and jury heard sworn testimony from the State's two most significant witnesses, Marion (M. C.) Perry during the morning session, and throughout the afternoon, the man who prosecutors had staked their only hope to convict Evans and Williams for first degree murder, the full confession of immunity-granted accomplice, Wade Levi Truett. Shortly after 9:00 AM, Merritt called Perry to the stand. In his direct Merritt addressed his witness as Mr. Perry, using such cordial words as "please" and "thank you" when asking him to explain his lawless history.

Merritt began, "Give us your full name if you will, please sir."

A: Marion Calvin Perry

Q: Where are you originally from, Mr. Perry?

A: Dawsonville, Dahlonega, Georgia.

Q: Is this your home?

A: That is where I was raised.

Q: Where you grew up?

A: Yes.

Q: Where are you staying right now, sir?

A: In jail.

Q: Are you a federal prisoner right now?

A: Yes, sir.

Q: A prisoner of the U.S. government?

A: Yes, sir.

Q: What are you in for, sir?

A: Violating the Internal Revenue laws [and] larceny of red liquor.

Q: And what did the revenue law violation consist of? What did you do to get that sentence?

A: Got caught in a still up here in Gwinnett County.

Q: All right, sir, and this sentence and the other one you referred to, how much time did you have to serve as a result of that?

A: I got two years on the hijacking of government liquor and twelve months on violating the Internal Revenue law.

Q: All right, sir. Have you ever had any other...been involved in any other violations of law?

A: Yes, sir.

Q: Tell us about them, if you will.

A: Been caught for numbers; larceny of automobiles; mostly liquor, whiskey.

Q: What we commonly call moonshine or white lightning?

A: That's right.

Q: Mr. Perry, have you been promised anything to come here to testify in court today in this matter?

A: No, sir.

Q: Have you been threatened or coerced or put under any duress?

A: No, sir.

Q: Have you been offered any immunity?

A: No, sir.

Q: And no promise of parole or any other kind of promise?

A: No, sir.

Perry was asked and answered questions about his interactions with Williams and Evans regarding their desire to have him steal an Oldsmobile for them. After Merritt finished his direct he turned Perry over to Thompson for cross. The politeness quickly came to an end.

Q: During Mr. Merritt's direct examination you stated your name as Marion Calvin Perry, is that correct?

A: Yes, that is my full name.

Q: Is that right?

A: As I said.

Q: Do you also identify yourself as M. C. Perry?

A: That is my name.

Q: That is your name?

A: That is what I go by.

Q: With reference to the past history you are giving us, when you first began testifying, you stated that you are serving time now for hijacking some red liquor and for Internal Revenue law violation, that is?

A: Yes.

Q: That you previously served time for numbers, just what is that, lottery operation?

A: Lottery.

Q: How many times have you been convicted of a lottery operation?

A: One time.

Q: You had been convicted of larceny of automobile. How many times have you been convicted of that?

A: One.

Q: And mostly your record was for manufacturing and transporting whiskey. How many times have you been convicted of those two offenses?

A: I don't know.

Q: Would you care to make an estimate of how many times you have been convicted?

A: Ten or fifteen times. Might have been more.

Q: Actually that is more or less your profession, making whiskey and stealing automobiles and operating a lottery?

A: Yes, sir.

Q: How old are you?

A: Twenty-eight.

Q: How much time have you served in jail?

A: I don't know about jail, but in the penitentiary…

Q: Well, jail or penitentiary?

A: You mean the time that I have got?

Q: How many years have you served in your career in the jail and penitentiary?

A: About seven or eight years.

Q: And you are twenty-nine now?

A: Twenty-eight.

Throughout Perry's testimony, opposing counsel objected to his answers. After overruling the defense time and again, mostly complaints of either leading the witness or claiming he was changing his answers as he went, Judge Pittard ran out of patience. "Gentlemen, let's don't argue about this anymore. You have this witness on the stand. The court is allowing you a thorough and sifting cross-examination, so let's proceed with it."

Thompson took one more jab at Judge Pittard. "I do not want to be in contempt of court's ruling, but I would like to make a statement in response to this, if the court please at the proper time."

Judge Pittard glared down at Thompson. "At the proper time you may do so, counselor, but for now let's proceed with this witness while he is on the stand and proceed with this trial."

Both counsels would spend all morning questioning Perry about his previous statements to investigators Homer Lee Cheek and Robert Hightower. The bulk of his testimony covered conversations with Williams and Evans a week before the murders and the chance meeting he had with Evans at Red's Service Station a few days after.

At the end of his testimony, M. C. Perry was released from court and taken by U.S. Marshals back to the Atlanta Federal Penitentiary. Lunch recess was called with jury members again cautioned not to discuss any trial matters during their break.

After lunch but before the bailiff brought in the jury, Solicitor Hames addressed the court. "Judge, before we call the next witness, there may be a matter I ought to take up outside the presence of the jury."

Judge Pittard said, "All right, you may."

"May it please the court, at this time the State intends to offer the testimony of the witness Wade Truett. Based upon a statement made to counsel and officers during the course of the investigation it has been determined by the state that upon the evidence corroborated in detail, he is not an actual perpetrator of the act but a principal in the second degree. Only by obtaining his testimony is it possible that those responsible for this crime can be brought to the bar of justice. We state in our place, and acting upon the rights and powers of the State under the common laws of this state and under the statutory authority, that the State has offered immunity to this witness. We say as a consideration to the state, the defendant has waived his right against self-incrimination as guaranteed by the Fifth Amendment of the Constitution of the United States and corresponding section of the Constitution of Georgia. We move that the statement of immunity and the guarantee offered him be spread on the minutes of this court in this case."

"Very well," the Judge said. "You may consider it so spread and in the record, Mr. Hames."

In both trials the defense strongly voiced its objection against the state calling Truett as a witness. Thompson said, "If it please the court, we would like to make a motion to exclude the testimony of Mr. Truett based on the grounds that the testimony he is to give and the statement or confession he has given is involuntary and coerced and that the witness has been promised a reward, immunity from prosecution, and been promised other immunities and other considerations in the form of monetary rewards for his testimony and confession."

Having planned from the beginning for this defense argument, Judge Pittard gave his short reply. "Motion overruled, Mr. Thompson. Bailiffs, please bring the jury in and let the defendant come in."

The courtroom settled into an absolute quiet. The trial and its outcome now hinged on the highly publicized, eagerly awaited testimony of the state's star witness.

Solicitor Merritt called Wade Levi Truett to the stand.

Two Gwinnett sheriff deputies escorted Truett into the filled courtroom. It was as quiet as a vacant tomb. Only the three men's shuffling footsteps on the wood floor disturbed the silence. Gradually, they made their way down the narrow center aisle. Court attendees turned sideways in their seats watching the three men pass. From news articles spectators knew him only by name. He wore a worn, loose-fitting suit. His shoulders slumped and he walked with short strides, his head slanted forward. He exhibited no remarkable features otherwise.

The men cleared the spectator pews nearly brushing against the defense table as they walked by. Truett passed within arm's length of Venson Williams. Neither made eye contact. Neither showed emotion.

The two deputies split off from their escort to take a seat, one against the wall near the judge's bench, one to the opposite side near the jury box. Truett stood in front of the judge's bench facing the clerk of court. With his right hand raised, left hand placed upon the Bible, Truett spoke aloud, solemnly swearing to be nothing but truthful lest forever be damned by Almighty God. He took his seat in the witness chair while looking out toward the spectators. He scanned the courtroom, unintentionally locking eyes with Williams, whom he'd accused of the cold-blooded murder of three county police officers, and then shifted his sunken eyes fearfully toward Judge Pittard. Pittard glimpsed back, showing no concern.

Merritt stood up from behind the prosecutor's table. He looked at Truett. The whole world would finally hear his story of that horrific April night in 1964. The state's entire case rested on what Truett was about to say. Of course Merritt had considered that a reward of immunity exchanged for "They done it, not me," testimony would, at the very least, open a sliver of doubt in a juror's mind. He believed Truett's testimony would be compelling enough to overcome any such bias, though, or so he hoped. Any trial lawyer will tell you that no verdict is ever in the bag because, when all is done, no matter how compelling the testimony, the jury's decision must be unanimous. Was Merritt confident about the hand he played in choosing the members of the jury?

Court spectators quietly settled in their seats as Merritt began his direct examination. In part, this is what Truett said.

Q: Give the court and jury your full name, please sir.

A: Wade Levi Truett

Q: Where are you from, Mr. Truett?

A: South Carolina, Hartsville.

Q: Is this your home?

A: Yes, sir.

Q: You lived there all your life?

A: Most of it, yes, sir.

Q: How old are you, Mr. Truett?

A: Thirty-four.

Q: Are you a U.S. federal prisoner now?

A: Yes, sir.

Q: What are you in federal prison for?

A: For conspiracy on a whiskey charge.

Q: Have you been convicted of any other crime?

A: Yes, sir, in nineteen forty-nine I was convicted of larceny, burglary. I have been convicted four or five times for forgery, burglary, conspiracy and larceny, I believe.

Q: How much time have you spent in prison?

A: I have pulled time on the chain gang in South Carolina and I have had a two-year sentence on this conspiracy charge which is about fourteen months now.

Q: Mr. Truett, right before this incident that you went to prison on, what sort of work were you doing?

A: I was running a partnership in a garage in South Carolina, Hartsville.

Q: With whom were you in partnership?

A: Venson Williams.

Q: What sort of work did you do there at the garage?

A: We bought and repaired wrecked automobiles.

Q: Mr. Truett, did you purchase all the automobiles you and Mr. Williams repaired at the garage?

A: Not all, no, sir.

Q: Not all. Could you tell the jury how you and Mr. Williams acquired automobiles if you didn't buy or purchase them?

A: Well, we stole 'em.

Q: How many cars did you and Venson steal?

A: We got several cars.

Q: When did you get in the stolen car business?

A: After the trial of the whiskey in Gainesville, Georgia, Venson and I got together and started when we rented the garage in South Carolina.

Q: And how long were you in the stolen car business before April of nineteen sixty-four?

The two men discussed the trivialities of car theft.

Mr. Merritt continued.

Q: Then where did you steal those cars?

A: Let me see, one in Charlotte, North Carolina, and two in Atlanta, I believe.

Q: Does that include the Oldsmobile?

A: I didn't steal the Oldsmobile; I just participated in it.

Q: How many automobiles did you participate in stealing?

A: I would say four in all, maybe five, maybe three, it wasn't very many.

Q: You just can't remember them all?

A: I didn't have that many to remember; was either four or five cars all together.

For the first twenty minutes of testimony, Truett was questioned about his criminal history and partnership with Venson Williams. After that, Merritt focused his direct line of questioning back to the salvaged 1963 Oldsmobile Arthur Hutchins saw inside the partners' Hartsville garage. Merritt then established the circumstances of that car as to why Truett and Williams sought to steal a similar Olds. He next connected the crime of grand theft auto with Alex Evans, who located and helped them steal the Oldsmobile found the next morning on Arc Road.

Over the next four hours, at times conferring with Luther Hames, Solicitor Merritt methodically walked Truett through the day of April 16 leading into those first few horror-filled hours just past midnight. Truett's memory required no deliberation. It was as if he were reliving yesterday, not a distant day one and a half years earlier. His testimony in remarkable detail captured the jury's full attention. Beginning from when he and Williams left Hartsville, South Carolina, for Atlanta, Truett told how Venson tried to phone Alex Evans but couldn't reach him. How they drove around Atlanta drinking beer, searching for but not finding the Oldsmobile they intended to steal. How they finally contacted Evans by phone and then later met him at the Moose Lodge. Truett described stealing the Oldsmobile and then driving to Arc Road in Gwinnett County. What they did on Arc Road before the policemen showed up. How Truett tried to get away but got caught. What the three of them and the three policemen did on top of the hill. He testified about how Evans talked to the policemen as if they were all friends. Of Evans taking full control by giving orders of who would do what. About moving his Impala Super Sport so he could back the patrol car into the woods and then driving over the hill when he heard the gunfire. He described seeing the Oldsmobile parked at the bottom of the hill. Watching Evans giving Williams a gun, taking bullets from one policeman's belt, loading the gun, and shooting another policeman two or three times point blank in his face. About getting his Chevy stuck in the ditch. Watching as Evans and Williams set the Oldsmobile on fire, leaving Arc Road, and taking Evans back to the Moose Lodge. And finally on the morning of April 17, back in Hartsville, how they threw their clothes and the Impala tires into Black Creek.

All through their direct examination Merritt and Hames meticulously covered every aspect of Truett's story. Of course during their cross-examination Dorsey and Thompson within their rights doubted all that Truett said, including every speck of integrity the man had since the day he was born. The state's star witness was unshakable. He never flinched. For certain, in the minds of those twelve men on the jury, he never lied. But perhaps

Truett's most convincing testimony, one that any reasonable man could appreciate, came during Solicitor Hames'
re-direct. This examination was for the sole purpose of
rebuking Thompson's objection in allowing Truett's testimony.

Q: Mr. Truett, when did you first decide that you
would give information to anyone in law enforcement
concerning your knowledge of this crime?

A: It was the last part of May nineteen sixty-five.

Q: Just exactly what promises were made to you in
order to secure your testimony and your confession?

A: The best I remember, exactly the way Robert Hightower put it to me, was if I would give a complete and
honest statement concerning everything I knew about
the death of these police officers out here, I mean, if I
did not actually participate in the actual shooting of the
police officers, immunity would be considered for it, if it
is verified that what I said is to be true and that I would
take a polygraph test to back up my statement and everything checks and found that way, then immunity will be
considered for me in this case.

Q: Did they promise you any reward money?

A: No, sir.

Q: Did you ask them for any?

A: No, sir.

Q: Were you promised you wouldn't be prosecuted
for participating in stealing the car, the sixty-three Oldsmobile?

A: I don't think that question was ever asked. I never
asked.

Q: You anticipate participating in the reward money?

A: I don't know; I haven't thought about it.

Q: You think you might get some of it for helping
solve this case?

A: I don't know.

Q: You would be entitled to. What would be your opinion?

A: I don't know. I don't have an opinion. I didn't do it for the reward.

Q: But it is your understanding from consulting with the solicitor general, Hightower, or whoever else you talked to about the case, you will not be prosecuted in any manner in connection with the murder of the policemen?

A: That is my understanding. Could be wrong.

Q: Were there any other promises made by anyone at any time in regards to you giving your full confession and your testimony made here in this court?

A: No, sir.

Q: Any written agreement of any kind ever entered into concerning this immunity?

A: Yes, sir, one was given to me later after I made a statement.

Q: Was this a typewritten document?

A: Yes, sir, I believe it was.

Q Who signed the document?

A: Mr. Reid Merritt. I believe his signature is on it. I didn't see him sign it.

Q: Do you recall the contents of it?

A: Not exactly, but I believe it says this is to certify that Wade L. Truett will be granted immunity in the death of the three, naming the three police officers and the date and so forth and so on, and that is about it.

Q: Mr. Truett, it was in reliance upon this understanding, this proposition, that you made your full statement concerning this to the officers, is that correct?

A: Yes, sir.

Q: Before you told them anything?

A: No, sir, I had made several statements before that concerning the fact that I didn't actually shoot the police officers.

Q: And it was after you were promised immunity that you gave the statement that in substance you have testified to today?

A: After they said they would consider immunity for me, and then I gave them a statement concerning what I said today.

Q: And later you were given some sort of a certificate of immunity?

A: Yes, sir.

Q: And you had relied upon that in making your statement to the officers and in testifying in this case, the fact you will not be prosecuted for the murders?

A: Yes, sir.

Q: But for that, you would not have made a statement and appeared here in this court to testify as a State witness in this crime, is that right?

A: Well now, to be right honest, that is a hard question to answer; I'm not sure. I had this thing on my mind for over a year, and honestly speaking I lost from one hundred seventy-six pounds down to one hundred forty-one pounds, and I believe in my own mind that even if I hadn't had my immunity or nothing else, I couldn't have went very much longer without telling somebody, because it was about to run me crazy. I couldn't sleep. I couldn't get it out of my mind what Venson and Alex done to those three policemen and the way they done it, and I know I was gonna go crazy, my own way of thinking.

Q: Then you don't know whether you would ever have given a confession?

A: Truthfully saying yes or no, I don't.

Q: It was the promise of immunity that motivated you in giving your statement and testimony?

A: Yes, sir.

Throughout the afternoon Truett described what would become a classic tale that forever changed not just Gwinnett but law enforcement worldwide. The lesson learned for cops became simply that nothing good ever happens when you give up your gun. Don't do it. But more important on that day, other than a cold, hard lesson for police, Truett's testimony convinced jurors that he was innocent of murder.

The defense counsel, and especially an indignant Alex Evans, publicly claimed that Truett was coached by the State to frame Evans. That it was done as a calculated attempt to divert attention from the guilt of a much larger conspiracy, one that implicated higher players in a state-run crime-organization. If such were true, though, why didn't they instruct Truett to say he saw not just Williams but Evans as well shoot all three police officers? It could have been easily woven into his testimony to say he did. To believe Truett was to believe there was no such ploy on the state's part or Truett's or anyone else's.

With the slight exception of M. C. Perry, no other witness who testified brought proof of Williams' guilt. Although several had already corroborated parts of Truett's statement, it was his testimony alone that would have to satisfy the State's indictment, but the defense had even less to counter the State. Attorney James Dorsey, as Merritt had predicted, offered Venson Williams as an unsworn witness in rebuttal to Wade Truett.

Dorsey asked the judge for about five minutes to make an opening position in the case.

Judge Pittard agreed.

"Gentlemen of the jury, the defendant would like to make a statement concerning his position too. The burden is now on us to go forward, and we will do so. With respect, I expect Mr. Williams make a statement to you and tell you his knowledge, or rather lack of knowledge, of these facts. I expect him to tell you and admit freely such things as are true concerning his relationship with this man Truett. I expect him to tell you he has known him for many years. He has been in business with him in South Carolina. I expect him to tell you, and I think you as intelligent gentlemen can realize, here is the man who a year and a half later is accused of a horrible crime on a given night in the spring of nineteen sixty-four. I expect Mr. Williams to tell you in his own words simply that he wasn't with this man Truett on this night. He knows nothing of this crime. This may seem a weak defense to you, but just remember, gentlemen, as you hear it, that the man who is connected with affairs of this night might have looked up alibis and explanations, but not a man who is going about his own business unaware that someday a year and a half later he will be called on to account for his actions on a given night. Listen to his brief statement and such other bits of evidence that we will bring to you here today. Gentlemen of the jury, thank you."

Dorsey addressed Judge Pittard, "If it please the court, I would appreciate the court instructing Venson Williams as to his legal rights with respect to the unsworn statement which he may make."

Judge Pittard acknowledged Dorsey by approving the protocol. "Mr. Williams I inform you that our law provides that in all criminal trials the prisoner has the right to make to the court and jury such statement as he may deem proper in his defense. The unsworn statement shall not be under oath and shall have only the force and weight as the jury think right to give it. The jury may believe it in preference to sworn testimony in the case. The prisoner shall not be compelled to answer any questions on cross examination, should he think proper to decline. You have the right under the law, and you make to the court and jury such statement in your behalf as you deem proper."

For the first time in his four-day trial, the jury and court heard Venson Williams explain in his own voice why he was completely innocent of this crime and the charge of first degree murder. His walk toward the witness stand was in a direct line to the clerk of court, who held out the Bible. Venson would not place his hand atop the Holy Scripture. He would not take the oath pledging to Almighty God that his words would be truthful. He took his seat in the witness box next to Judge Pittard.

Reading from prepared notes, Williams stated his version of events surrounding April 16 and 17, 1964. "Gentlemen of the jury, first of all I am not guilty of this crime that I am accused of. I'm married and born and raised in Dawson County, Georgia, and have been living in Atlanta for the past ten or twelve years. I always have bought and sold cars, worked at car lots, and stuff like that. I was in business, the garage business, with Wade Truett up in South Carolina. We were buying used cars from up North and bringing them back and fixing them up and we also would buy some wrecked cars and rebuild them and sell them. It was a perfectly legitimate business. At no time did we ever do anything outside of the law. This has been some year and a half ago. I can't remember just exactly where I was or have a pat alibi. I am assuming I was home. My wife and mother-in-law would have been the only people that could vouch for me that night, but they don't remember back to that exact night.

"I don't think I was in the Atlanta area, or I would have been reading about it in the newspapers. But I don't remember reading the Atlanta papers about it.

"Of course I do remember hearing about it, but there was no specific point in time, so I must have been on my way to New York. If it is something that happened next door to me, it would be more clear in my mind, but we read and hear every day in newspapers about some crime committed somewhere or other, and it just doesn't bring it close to home enough for me to remember where I was at that specific time, so I have no reason to pinpoint myself at any certain event that happened some year and a half ago. Had I been approached a few days following that, I'm sure I could have remembered, and it would have been clear in my mind, but since it has been so long that this actually happened, I just don't recall exactly where I was, so I have no reason to remember it.

"And I don't remember just exactly what time I got back up to South Carolina the next day. We went a few days after that to New York and bought cars and brung them back, which we did on numerous occasions. And that is about the extent of my activities that I can recall around in that area of time.

"I just want to say again that I am not guilty of committing any crime at that time or anything like that, and I realize it's a serious crime that I am charged with, but it isn't true. No part of it is. It is just a shock to me and beyond me that I could even believe that I could be accused of anything of this nature and just a shock to all my neighbors and everyone that knows me. No one could believe that I could be guilty of such a thing, and the whole extent of this accusation against me is all untrue. There is not a bit of truth in it, and I wish to make you gentlemen aware of that fact, that I was not guilty of anything like that at all. It wouldn't be—it's just unbelievable. That is all. It's just, it just couldn't happen. I'm not guilty."

In support of Williams' statement and to dispute both M. C. Perry and Wade Truett's testimony, Dorsey asked to bring Evans to the stand, but defense attorney Robert Thompson interrupted. "Excuse me, Mr. Dorsey. Your Honor, if it pleases the court, we represent Mr. Evans, who is a co-indictee in this trial. Mr. Evans has been advised of his constitutional rights to refuse to testify in this or any other case on the grounds his testimony might incriminate him. He has waived any right that he has under the constitution in that regard, as he feels his testimony would not incriminate him."

The judge nodded. "All right, Counselor, will you please proceed? Call your witness."

Evans was sworn in before the prosecutor began his questioning.

Q: Mr. Evans, would you give your full name?

A: Alex S. Evans.

Q: Mr. Evans, where is your home?

A: Buford, Georgia.

Q: How long have you lived in Buford and Gwinnett County?

A: Since May of nineteen fifty-six.

Q: Where were you a native of, where were you born?

A: Born in Oconee County, Bishop, Georgia.

Q: You are a native Georgian?

A: Yes, sir.

Q: You remember the occasion on which three police officers met their death in Gwinnett County?

A: Yes, sir.

Q: Prior to that occasion, did you know a man named M. C. Perry?

A: Yes, sir. I've known him since nineteen fifty-six when I went to work for the state.

Q: Prior to the middle of April nineteen sixty-four, within a month or two, what occasions if any had you seen or talked to M. C. Perry?

A: Last time I saw Perry was the day previous to him turning in to the penitentiary on two charges he had convictions. Previous to that it had been some months, two or three months since I had seen him.

Q: Had you had any telephone conversations with him during those two or three months?

A: No. After that day I had no other conversation with him.

Q: Will you please tell this jury whether or not you discussed with Perry any plan to steal any automobile or automobiles?

A: Any plans for me to steal any automobiles?

Q: Or for him to or anyone, the two of you, to cause it to be done or be connected with it? Did you have any such conversation with M. C. Perry?

A: About he and I stealing automobiles?

Q: Yes, sir.

A: No, sir, I did not.

Q: Did you talk to him about Oldsmobile automobiles or getting an automobile?

A: No, sir, we had no such conversation.

Q: All right, sir. Now, coming down to April sixteen, of nineteen sixty-four, Mr. Evans, during the course of that day and that afternoon, will you tell this jury in your own words beginning any time you want, afternoon or early afternoon of that day, where you were, what you were doing?

A: Sometime shortly after noon a fellow by the name of Lott came to my house and asked me to ride with him down into Rockdale County. I was down there with Lott at this motel until nearly, I would say around eight o'clock in the evening, when we left and drove right straight back to my home. Got there I would say between eight—between eight-thirty and nine o'clock. I don't know the exact time, between those times.

Q: Did you leave your home during the course of that evening?

A: No, sir, I did not.

Q: Did you go anywhere during the course of that evening with a man named Wade Levi Truett?

A: No, sir.

Q: Do you know Wade Levi Truett?

A: I only know a Wade Levi Truett from his record and reputation in the papers and conviction on a tractor-trailer thing with Perry and other people. I don't know him personally. I don't know him personally to see him, no, sir.

Q: Were you with him on—any time on the day of April sixteen, nineteen sixty-four, or that night or the— any of the hours of April seventeen nineteen sixty-four?

A: No, sir, I don't know if I would know the man if I were to see him to his face; I couldn't say. I couldn't say I have ever seen the man on any occasion.

Q: Do you know a man named Venson Eugene Williams, who is on trial here today?

A: Yes, sir, I know him.

Q: How well do you know him? Over what period of time had you known him?

A: To know him, to speak to him, I have spoken to him about three or four different occasions. I knew him, having seen him in the previous years, but I had no conversation with him.

Q: No personal acquaintance?

A: No, sir.

Q: On the sixteenth of April, nineteen sixty-four, that afternoon or evening or on into the morning hours of the seventeenth, were you with Venson Williams?

A: I didn't leave my home, Mr. Dorsey. After I came in from Rockdale County I never left my home that evening or that night, so I was not with anybody except my family.

Q: Within the period of a month prior to those dates, had you had any occasion to have a telephone conversation with Venson Williams?

A: I have never talked on the telephone to Venson Williams, no, sir. I have never had an occasion to talk with him on the telephone, no, sir.

Q: Did Venson Williams ever ask you to locate any automobile for him, particularly any Oldsmobile?

Hames objected. "If Your Honor please, this is his witness. He is leading and suggesting the answer."

Judge Pittard answered, "Yes, I do think the form of your question is leading, Mr. Dorsey, and suggestive of the answer you expect from the witness."

Dorsey said, "Yes, sir."

"The same rule would apply to you as the others," added the judge.

"Yes, sir." He turned to his client. "I will ask you whether or not you ever had any conversation with him relative to any matter touching on the theft of an automobile."

A: No, sir, I have not.

Q: Mr. Evans, what is the first knowledge you had of the death of these officers?

A: The morning of April seventeen.

Q: Had you known those men personally?

A: Yes, sir, very well.

Q: How long had you known them?

A: I worked real close with them from nineteen sixty-one, from January up until the time, let's see, I believe August, nineteen sixty-two, when I resigned from the Sheriff's Department. I knew them real well, yes.

Q: Did you have any occasion to participate in any investigation concerning their deaths?

A: Yes, sir, I did.

Q: What did you do?

A: I had received some information regarding an Oldsmobile which was another sixty-three Oldsmobile, and I investigated that because a person came to me and said that Mrs. Davis or a relative of Mrs. Davis would—said…

Hames interrupted. "Your Honor, any conversation with some supposed informer would be hearsay on the part of this witness."

Judge Pittard agreed. "I think so. I think the witness would be precluded from going into any conversation he has had with any other person. You can testify from your own knowledge, Mr. Evans, and not what somebody else told you."

"Yes, sir."

Q: Mr. Evans, limiting yourself to what you know or did, would you tell us what investigation you did make of what actually did take…

Hames jumped in. "If it please the court, what he did here after the commission of the crime would be self-serving and we object."

Judge Pittard said. "The court will allow him to answer that question, Mr. Hames."

Q: "All right, Alex, please continue." Dorsey said.

A: "I began to check around to see what I could find out because I had voluntarily came over here after they called my house, GBI called, and I came over here to be questioned myself. I guess everybody was a suspect. I know I was, and I came over here and I answered their questions and then I begin to check around after this thing started, and I found out about an Oldsmobile which was identical in style and body and what have you that was sold…"

Hames shook his head. "Your Honor, the fact—that would be hearsay."

"Yes, sir, I do not see—can you show any relevancy in this testimony in the case on trial, Mr. Dorsey?"

"If it please the court the basis of the relevancy would be the extent of knowledge of this man who has been accused of this crime, of anything concerning it, and I think his conduct…"

"All right, I will hear that testimony. This other statement, this private investigation on his part and his actions as such, I do not think is relevant to this matter."

"All right, sir." Dorsey continued. "Mr. Evans, one further question. How did you first have knowledge of the death of these officers?"

A: People calling, and then my father called me from Athens, and different people in the county called me.

Q: Don't go into what any of them said.

A: No, sir.

Q: All right, Mr. Evans. Would you please tell this court and jury, did you participate in any events during the nights of the sixteenth and seventeenth of April, nineteen sixty-four, leading up to or concerning the death of these officers?

A: No, sir, I did not.

Dorsey walked back to his defense table scowling impolitely at the solicitor. "Witness is with you."

Outraged by the most grievous case of perjury he'd ever heard on the witness stand, Luther Hames quickly rose from his chair and began his cross-examination from behind the prosecutor's table.

Q: Mr. Evans, if you were on Arc Road approximately one thirty on the morning of the seventeenth day of April and you held in your hand one of these pistols here, and you fired one or more of these guns into the body of these three officers, would you tell this jury that you did?

A: I stated, Mr. Hames, that I didn't leave my home. I did not have a pistol. I was not on Arc Road, and I did not shoot any policeman.

Q: I say, if you had, would you have told this jury?

A: There is no way for me to put myself in a position that I can answer that because I was not there.

Shaking his head in disgust Hames closed his brief fiery cross-examination shouting loudly, "That's all I have with this witness, Your Honor."

For their next witness the defense called Calvin Perry. He was the grandfather of M. C. Perry. Thompson questioned the senior Perry as to his grandson's character and honesty.

Q: Mr. Perry, what is your age, sir?

A: Which?

Q: What is your age?

A: I'm going on seventy-four.

Q: Where do you live, Mr. Perry?

A: I live in the edge of Lumpkin County, four miles above Dawsonville.

Q: Do you know M. C. Perry?

A: Yeah.

Q: Is there any relationship between you and M. C.?

A: I'm his Grandaddy.

Q: How long have you known M. C.?

A: I have knowed him ever since he was born.

Q: State whether or not he ever lived with you.

A: He has been off and on all his life.

Q: At your residence?

A: Which?

Q: Living at your house all his life?

A: Well, part of the time, yeah.

Q: Do you know his reputation in the community where he lives?

A: Do which?

Q: Do you know his reputation, Mr. Perry, in the community where he lives?

A: It ain't so good.

Q: Do you know what it is? Is his reputation good or bad?

A: Bad.

Q: Mr. Perry, do you know his reputation for being truthful?

A: Well, sometimes be truthful and sometimes won't.

Q: Do you know his general reputation for being truthful at all?

Hames interrupted Thompson's examination. "Your Honor, I think-…"

Again irritated by the constant objections from the prosecution, the judge said, "Mr. Hames, I understand where you're going here." His stare focused on the defense attorney. "Counselor, I think you have asked the statutory question."

"Your Honor, my understanding [of] the statutory question is: Do you know his reputation in the community where he lives for being truthful and honest?"

Pittard replied, "No, sir! My understanding is, 'Do you know his reputation.' You can ask whether it is good or bad or not, Mr. Thompson." After a very brief but noticeable pause, the judge politely told the ferocious defense attorney, "Will you please continue your direct."

A moderate hum of distraction rumbled among the courtroom spectators. The elder Perry was not meeting the defense's attempt at disputing the earlier testimony of his grandson.

Thompson resumed his direct questioning.

Q: Based upon his reputation, Mr. Perry, would you believe M. C. Perry on oath?

A: I don't think so.

Sensing no claim of victory with his defense witness, Thompson woefully turned to a smiling Luther Hames. "He is with you."

Hames began with, "You say you are his grandfather?"

A: Yes, sir.

Q: You reared him?

A: Which?

Q: You reared him, you raised him?

A: No, I didn't exactly raise him.

Q: He was around your house all the time, wasn't he?

A: Which?

Q: Around your house?

A: Around there, yeah.

Q: Well, where did he learn not to tell the truth?

A: I don't know about that.

Hames said, "Mr. Perry, please come down from the stand."

"Didn't learn him nothing as far as that part," the grandfather declared. He remained in the witness chair.

The solicitor called out in a demanding voice, "Mr. Perry, please come down from the stand!" Pushing proper courtroom etiquette to its limit Hames looked up at the ceiling, closed his eyes, and shook his head. As he returned to the prosecutor's table, he informed Judge Pittard, "Your Honor, I have no further questions for this witness."

As Grandpa Perry wandered down from the witness stand, spectators erupted in laughter. Pounding his gavel several times the judge shouted, "As I had warned this court earlier, and I now say under great annoyance, this trial is not being conducted for any exhibition. The court cannot and will not tolerate any further show of emotion whatsoever from the audience. If necessary I will clear the courtroom of all spectators for the duration of this trial!"

***

One month later, Alex Evans, charged with first-degree murder of Officer Jerry Everett, stood before Judge Pittard, a twelve-man jury, prosecutors, and a packed courtroom. Key witnesses repeated their testimony as before, and Evans' sworn testimony recurred almost word for word, Truett, as he had pointed his finger at Venson Williams in the first trial, did so again at Alex Evans in the second trial. Both trials ran a four-day course, but unlike the festive atmosphere for Williams, hostile courtyard observers booed and hissed every time U.S. Marshals escorted the well-known Alex Evans to and from the courthouse.

Toward the end of the trial, defense attorney Robert Thompson called Alex Evans' son to the witness stand. The attorney asked the boy, also known as Alex, "Do you know where you were on April sixteen of nineteen sixty-four?"

A: To start off with, I was out riding around with some friends, and then we come home, just about dark, and Daddy was laying on the couch at home and Mama was sitting in the chair and they were watching some program, I don't know exactly what it was, some program that Mama fusses about seeing every time because we like to see something else on TV, a western or something. Some doctor picture, I think, I'm not sure.

Q: What time that night did you go to bed, Alex?

A: It was after, I believe it was after the news came on, just coming on.

Q: The news was coming on when you went to bed?

A: Yes.

Q: Where was your father then?

A: He was still in the living room with my mother.

Q: Your mother was there too?

A: Uh-huh.

Q: How do you know this was April sixteen of last year when this happened?

A: The next day when I went to school, a friend of mine, Roger Everett, somebody was talking about, they called him at the office or something. I don't remember exactly how it got out around school, something about his brother or somebody kin to him had been shot, policeman got killed, and when I got home, I told—after Mama and Daddy got home, I was talking to them about it, and they had already knowed it.

Q: In regards to the night of April sixteen, nineteen sixty-four, do you know whether or not your father left the house after eleven o'clock?

A: I don't know whether he did or not because I don't—I don't believe he did. He didn't usually leave that late.

Q: Your answer then is you don't know whether he left after eleven o'clock that night?

A: Yes, sir.

Following the boy's testimony, Alex Evans' wife was called to the witness stand.

Q: Do you know where Alex was on the night of April sixteen, nineteen sixty-four?

A: I don't know where he was that afternoon. I know where he was that night.

Q: What time after evening or night did you see him?

A: He came in shortly after eight thirty.

Q: Please state whether or not you were there when he came in that evening.

A: Yes, I was there. I was watching television.

Q: You recall anything he did that evening?

A: He came and ate, lay down on the couch, which was normal, and spent most of the evening there till we went to bed, till he went to bed.

Q: What time did he go to bed, if you know?

A: I would say in the neighborhood of between eleven and twelve o'clock.

Q: Do you know whether or not he left the house that night?

A: He didn't leave, to my knowledge; he was there when I got up the next morning.

Q: Were you up when he went to bed, or did you go to bed at the same time?

A: I was up when he went to bed.

Q: Did you go to bed at the same time?

A: No, he went to bed before I did.

Q: What time did you go to bed that night?

A: I would say in the neighborhood of about one o'clock; after the late show went off.

Q: Would you state whether or not he left the house at any time?

A: No, he didn't.

Q: Do you sleep in the same bed with Alex?

A: Yes.

Q: Do you know whether or not he got up any time during the night?

A: No, he didn't get up.

In another brief cross-examination, Solicitor Hames questioned the witness. Although Mrs. Evans had taken an oath to be truthful, Hames recognized that she was not the defendant on trial. Having no desire to accuse her in any way, Hames kindly proceeded and she politely answered.

Q: Mrs. Evans, you say when your husband came home on the night of April sixteen, nineteen sixty-four at approximately eight-thirty or shortly thereafter, you were watching television?

A: Yes, sir.

Q: And you are testifying that he did not leave your house after he came home that night?

A: Yes, sir.

Q: Tell me, Mrs. Evans, are you sure, without any doubt, that Alex did not leave the house that night?

A: To the best of my knowledge, he did not.

There was no need to continue what might seem an interrogation of Mrs. Evans. Any further questions regarding her husband's whereabouts that murderous April night could suggest that the State was accusing her as an accessory in a cover-up conspiracy to conceal her husband's guilt by contributing to his alibi which an objective Southern juror might conclude as a loyal spousal obligation. The solicitor had no intention of falsely holding her accountable.

Hames took a long, hard stare at the jury, expressing without words an understanding that they would be unbiased with no inference outside her testimony. Facing Mrs. Evans, he gestured a kind nod of respect and then informed Judge Pittard, "The State has no further questions for this witness."

From the stand, Mrs. Evans walked alone between the crowded pews that filled the courtroom's length. Her composure reflected a quiet sadness as she passed through.

The courtroom atmosphere markedly changed when Alex Evans was called to deliver his unsworn statement, but first, as Dorsey had asked Judge Pittard to instruct Venson Williams in the first trial, so too did Thompson ask that his client be instructed to his legal rights in the co-trial.

Judge Pittard stated, "Mr. Evans, the court gives you the right to make to the court and jury such statement in your own behalf as you see fit. It need not be under oath, and you need not be subject to cross-examination. You may make such statement as you see fit in your behalf."

Alex walked toward the witness stand. He passed the Bible without swearing the oath. Jury members looked upon him in harsh disapproval. Evans sat down in the witness chair. He spoke in an uncharacteristically soft, almost inaudible, voice. "Thank you, Your Honor, gentlemen of the jury."

Thompson interrupted his client. "Speak a little louder, Alex."

"First of all let me say I don't know why I am here exactly, but I am going to do everything I can to show you why I have been indicted. When these murders happened, these three friends of mine who I worked very close with and were close friends, especially Jerry and Ralph, I knew Mr. Gravitt, he was a good friend of mine…"

Robert Thompson interrupted his client. "Your Honor, can we turn up the amplifier? Alex, could you please speak a little louder?"

Judge Pittard requested, "Mr. Evans, if you will speak loud enough so the jurors can hear what you have to say. You may now continue."

"The night that these murders happened I was at home. I got home shortly after eight thirty, between eight thirty and nine o'clock, I'm not sure. I was not away from my home that night. The next morning when I got up the phone began to ring, people calling me and telling me about these murders, and that is when I asked my wife what time was it when I came in. She said 'Doctor

Kildare' had just come on. Of course I didn't like the program, and I had lain down on the couch."

Thompson spoke up. "Your Honor, I do hate to continue interrupting, but Alex, you are going to have to speak louder, please."

"After some time had passed, during the next morning, even my father called me from Athens and asked me about it, who it was that had been killed. At that time I did not know; it was not on the news. Sometime after that time that the investigation surrounding the murders I was called, I was called and a number left at my residence for me to call and I called it, and it was over here at the City Hall in Lawrenceville where the investigation was taking place at that time. I came over here in response to that call from the GBI. I answered each and every question they asked me. I went back home. Some time passed, and a neighbor and friend of mine came to me shortly after that, and he said, 'Alex, relatives of Ralph wish you would take a part in this investigation.'"

Solicitor Hames interrupted the proceedings. "If it please the court, I realize he is making a statement, but the defendant cannot use his statement as a vehicle to introduce improper evidence that would be hearsay. I think, while he is entitled to make a statement in his own behalf, he can't go outside the rules of evidence."

Judge Pittard noted, "Continue with your statement, Mr. Evans, and if you will, confine your statement to relative facts concerning whatever you wish to say relative to this offense."

Evans answered, "Your Honor, that is exactly what I want. I want the truth to come out here. I say the truth as to me has not come out, other than what I am telling you."

Any credibility his alibi gained from his wife's testimony was quickly lost on the jury as Evans continued his statement in wandering detail, returning to his earlier claims of the so-called Gwinnett crime syndicate. Holding back nothing, he provided the dirt on how the "Crime Machine" operated and names of those in its chain of command, including county officials. "These were the men who committed this horrible crime! It was a conspiracy to silence those police officers for what they knew."

Following that accusation, he boldly called out two men the "Syndicate" hired to mete out its murderous plot. Making matters worse he crowed about his achievements in and out of law enforcement, specifically his actions in maintaining an honorable existence between criminals and the law. In a last-ditch effort to confuse anyone still listening, Evans laid out a timeline to his own investigation, wholly absent of any substance, and how he would have solved the crime if allowed.

Finally, one hour after he began, Alex Evans concluded his statement before a dismayed but highly appreciative jury. Before leaving the witness box he made one final plea for the jury's sympathy by shouting brazen denials. "The connections between those cases I've described that are down there on the gambling, the armed robbery cases, between the gambling cases, between the local car rackets, and the names that I have named, you will find that the whole truth has not come out.

"I was not there! I have never talked on the phone to Williams or Truett. I did not take part in any murders. I have never mistreated a man as a previous officer, even this man on the stand, Perry, but he doesn't like me. He doesn't like me! I have made cases against him, but I didn't mistreat him. I have never threatened M. C. Perry in any way. I have never threatened Williams. I have never threatened Truett. I did not meet those people that night. I have never talked to them on the telephone. I was not involved in this murder in any way. I tell you the only reason I'm indicted is because of what I was doing, and I think if you gentlemen will take it on yourselves to sometime check into what I've said about these murders, it's the truth, so help me God. I didn't do it! I have never shot a man."

Judge Pittard stared at the pleading defendant. "Is that all you wish to say?"

"Yes, sir."

"All right, come down."

Although Georgia law allows for a defendant to give the jury an unsworn statement, Southern rule does not. As was the case with Williams, Evan's unsworn statement had no impact on the jury. Nonetheless, Merritt called several witnesses for rebuttal. He proved through hard facts that what Evans had said was pure fantasy and his empty accusations against those who were not involved were just that, empty. Against this rebuttal the defense had nothing left in pleading its case to the jury.

Both the state and defense rested. Judge Pittard called for a fifteen-minute break. At three o'clock in the afternoon on the fourth day of the second trial, jurors would hear from the attorneys for the last time.

Merritt said in his closing argument, "A trial is a sacred thing, the backbone of freedom in our great country. One of the things that makes America great is that all defendants are innocent and will remain innocent until they are proven guilty beyond any reasonable doubt. On the other hand, if any or all of the accused men are found guilty of the crime of murder, then any or all of them should be dealt with to the fullest extent allowed by our law."

With a fierce conclusion to his argument against the defendant, Merritt told the jury, "Alex Evans should be put to death!" Quoting freely from the Bible to back up his stand, Merritt cited Jesus Christ's Sermon on the Mount. "You shall not murder! Anyone who murders will be subject to judgment! Alex Evans has sowed the evil fruit and he shall reap!"

In his closing argument rebuttal to Merritt, defense attorney Dorsey said, "I have been a prosecuting attorney for a number of years, and I myself have asked for the death penalty many a time, but in all those years I have never heard the death penalty asked for in the name of our Savior Jesus Christ.

"Good men of the jury, you should not convict Mr. Evans on the testimony of Wade Truett alone, he being a convicted man now serving federal time. His testimony has been solely based upon his offered and accepted immunity. I believe cash and other rewards as well. Investigators chose Truett, telling him, 'Just tell us you didn't do it and give us the men we want.' The state has coached his statements, which contain glaring errors in fact, and the state is now prosecuting not the men responsible for this heinous crime but the men they want to take blame. All the terrible power of the state has been invoked against Mr. Evans. If you fine men of the jury cannot overlook this devious attempt to implicate Mr. Evans, then you should hand him mercy, if you see fit to convict him."

In rebuttal to Dorsey's claim and request to the jury, Luther Hames shouted in his dramatic style, "Speak not to me of mercy! When a man kills for the almighty dollar, that is ghastly. That is inhumane. Mercy can be granted only to those who give it. In this case none was handed to those three officers, so you should hand none to this defendant in exchange. The only way to teach the criminal is by swift and certain punishment. Murder shall be met with death! These murders descended upon Gwinnett County a dark pall over property and personal lives that are all now less secure since these slayings. Let justice be done though the heavens fall!"

The twelve-man jury was not swayed by religious beliefs but rather proven guilt over presumed innocence, in this case, Truett's testimony. But in this case, jurors were forced to consider that he was a killer, not because he fired the fatal bullets, but by reason of conspiracy: participation in the crime of stealing a car that led to a triple murder during that crime and a cover up afterwards. And they had to consider Truett's motivation for testifying. They had two choices: what he said from the stand, "I had this thing on my mind for over a year, and honestly speaking, I believe in my own mind that even if I hadn't had my immunity or nothing else, I couldn't have went very much longer without telling somebody, because I know I was gonna go crazy." Or did he testify as Dorsey had reasoned, for offers of cash and other rewards in a devious scheme by the state: "Just tell us you didn't do it and give us the men we want."

After the smoke from the closing arguments had cleared, Judge Pittard explained to jurors the Charge of the Court. It was a lengthy order of law that he had to present in layman's terms, a difficult challenge, considering the possible outcome of a death sentence and the fact that the case contained evidence only from a conspirator's confession. The charge, given in each trial, was the essence of the American judicial system.

"Gentlemen of the jury, you have been trying the case of the state against Alex S. Evans, who is charged in this joint indictment along with Venson Eugene Williams with the offense of murder, a violation of the criminal laws of the State of Georgia.

"This case came before you by virtue of an indictment returned by the grand jury of this county. The indictment charges that he did on the seventeenth day of April, nineteen sixty-four, unlawfully with malice afore-thought kill and murder one Jerry R. Everett by then and there shooting him with a pistol.

"I caution you gentlemen of the jury that an indict-ment does not constitute evidence nor does the fact that a grand jury has returned an indictment against the de-fendant constitute any evidence or inference of guilt. It is merely the manner in which the charge is brought before the court for trial on its merits, as revealed in your pres-ence and hearing.

"The defendant has filed his plea of not guilty to this indictment whereby he denies the charge and places the burden on the state to prove its case under instructions given you by the Court.

"In criminal cases, gentlemen, you are the judges of both the law and the facts. This defendant enters upon this trial with the presumption of innocence in his favor, and this presumption remains with him until and unless the state shall overcome and remove it by the introduc-tion of evidence and proof to you sufficient to convince your minds to a moral and reasonable certainty and be-yond a reasonable doubt of the guilt of the accused.

"The burden of proof is on the state to prove every material allegation in this indictment. Under our law in no sense is the defendant required to prove that he is innocent. As stated, he is presumed to be and remains so until the state proves his guilt, not by a mere prepon-derance of the evidence as in civil cases, but beyond a reasonable doubt."

Judge Pittard then gave a synopsis of the crime the jury members were to consider: "Where several persons conspire to engage in unlawful acts of larceny of motor vehicles and in pursuance of the common design, one of the conspirators locates the said vehicle and said conspirator, in the company of the other conspirators, goes to the location of the said vehicle, makes inoperable the security devices thereof, and these conspirators steal said vehicle and drive the same to another location, and while they are engaged in concealing the identity of said vehicle and removing identifications and security devices from said vehicle in furtherance of the design to steal said motor vehicle and are confronted by officers of the law, that thereafter in furtherance of their design to steal the aforesaid motor vehicle, and to conceal the identity of the conspirators and to make escape from the custody of the said officers, one or more of the conspirators shoots and kills said officers, such killing is the probable consequence of the unlawful design to steal said motor vehicle, and all of the conspirators are guilty of murder. It is not necessary that the crime of murder be a part of the original design, but it is enough if it be one of the incidental probable consequences of the execution of their design and should appear at the moment to one of the participants to be expedient for the common purpose. The intent of the actual slayer is imputable to his co-conspirators."

He then continued a lengthy explanation to what the legal meaning was for conspiracy, the state's right to grant immunity to a witness of equal guilt for his testimony, and the rightful matters of law as it pertained to the defendants and prosecutors.

Judge Pittard finally concluded by explaining, "Whatever your verdict may be, gentlemen, let it speak the truth, for that is what the word verdict means, the spoken truth of the case. Let it be written upon the back of this indictment which you will have out with you, let it be dated and signed by one of your members as foreman and returned into court."

In Venson Williams' trial the jury deliberated for one hour. In Alex Evans' trial the jury deliberated for three hours.

❧

In each trial when court reconvened, Judge Pittard asked, "Gentlemen of the jury, have you arrived at a verdict in this case?"

The jury foreman responded, "We have, Your Honor."

"Before this verdict is received, let the court caution the audience that there shall be no show of emotion and no outbursts of any kind. Mr. Solicitor, you may receive the verdict."

In each case, Mr. Merritt stood and read the report from the jury, given to him from their foreman. "We, the jury, find the defendant guilty."

Judge Pittard ordered, "Let that verdict be received." After each trial he gave the jury its final order, and praise. "Mr. Foreman and gentlemen of the jury, the court will now be able to discharge you from further service during this term of court. I hope your service during this term has not been too great an inconvenience. I know it is rather harsh to require you to remain away from your families, but the court thanks you for your service as jurors and your attention to detail that you have devoted to your service. I am glad that we have in this county the jurors that we do have. I'm sincerely proud of the jurors in this county and the citizens of our county and the way you have responded to your service. With the sincere thanks of the court, you are excused."

After the jury had left the Courtroom, Judge Pittard asked Dorsey in the Williams trial as he did Thompson in the Evans trial, "Is there any reason why sentence should not be imposed in this case?"

In each trial both defense attorneys replied, "No, sir."

Judge Pittard told each man, "Let the defendant stand. The jury has found you guilty in this case without a recommendation. It therefore becomes mandatory upon this court as a matter of law to impose the following sentence: It is considered, ordered, and adjudged by the court that the defendant be taken from the bar of this court to the common jail of Gwinnett County until his removal therefrom to the custody of the director of the State Department of Corrections for the purpose of the execution of this sentence in the manner prescribed by law. On the thirtieth day of November, nineteen sixty-five, between the hours of ten o'clock AM and two o'clock PM, defendant Venson Eugene Williams [and, at the end of his trial one month later, Alex S. Evans] shall be electrocuted by the director of the State Department of Corrections. May God have mercy on your soul."

After hearing his sentence, an emotionless Alex Evans was escorted from the courthouse by four Gwinnett sheriff deputies, his former law enforcement partners. The Justice Building's rear exit doors abruptly opened. Deputies quickly marched Evans out into the dimming afternoon sunlight. In the midst of their hurried pace he jerked his entourage to a full stop. From the veranda's back steps he slowly gazed at the returning gawk of onlookers gathered in the packed courtyard. They had eagerly waited eighteen months and four days for this moment.

Since his dismissal from the sheriff's department twenty months before, Evans' hairline had receded into a bald patch crowning his head. His weight had diminished so that the fitted gray suit he wore draped from his slumping shoulders as if still on its coat hanger. Alex raised his handcuffed wrists high above his head in a last public gesture of defiance.

The hostile crowd jeered and cat-whistled in joyful objection. Jerking him more forcefully than he had them, deputies loaded Evans into the backseat of a Gwinnett sheriff patrol car then sped away. Many spectators noted the irony that the patrol car that took him away was the very same one Alex himself had driven while with the sheriff's department. Perhaps the vehicle choice was a last public gesture from his former partners.

Through court appeals, both Alex Evans' and Venson Williams' death sentences were commuted to life in prison with the possibility of parole. In 1989, after serving twenty-five years in prison, Williams walked through the gates of Reidsville State Penitentiary a free man. He was given a ten-year probation term. Reporters standing at the gate asked him for any comments regarding the crime or the twenty-five years of his life he'd spent behind bars. He replied, "I will not ever talk to you about my past. I will only thank the good Lord for this day and any more days he sees fit to give me."

Venson Williams died of natural causes in 2015. He lived up to his promise. He never again spoke of that murderous April night in 1964.

After several attempts before the Parole Board, Alex Evans never received a favorable decision. He told anyone who would listen, "I don't care to be paroled. I am not guilty of the crime for which I am serving. The only justice for me is a full pardon." Alex got part of his wish; he did not get parole. He spent more than fifty years as an inmate in the Georgia Department of Corrections, becoming the state's longest-serving prisoner of all time. He died in prison in May 2017. He was ninety-one years of age.

In 1986 Wade Truett, driving alone late at night, was killed when his car skidded off a rural Cobb County road and hit an oak tree. His body, partially ejected through the windshield, was not discovered for several days.

ɔ

Shortly after the trials ended, John Crunkleton was appointed by Gwinnett County commissioners as Chief of Police. He honorably served in that position for sixteen years, longer than anyone before him. Known as the Father of Gwinnett Police he developed the department into one of the nation's finest police forces, a distinction still held and admired to this day. As a formality of indoctrination, Chief Crunkleton required all newly sworn officers be taken to Arc Road their first night on duty. The rookie had to walk the road's full two-mile length. Halfway along, where once stood the old field house, they would inscribe their initials into the oak tree where, a few feet away, three of their law enforcement brothers paid the ultimate lawman's oath with their lives.

Reid Merritt served as Gwinnett County Solicitor General and later as County District Attorney from 1965 to 1972. He was elected Superior Court Judge and served in that high honor until 1986. Judge Merritt passed away in 2008 and will always be remembered for his successful prosecution of these two trials and his devotion to the Gwinnett County judicial system.

In recognition of his successful investigation in this case, Robert Hightower was awarded Georgia Bureau of Investigation Agent of the Year. He left the GBI for his beloved Cobb County, taking the position of Police Chief and then later became the first director of the county's Department of Public Safety. In 1999 Hightower accepted an appointment from Georgia Governor Roy Barnes as Colonel of the State Patrol and one year later was appointed as commissioner of the Department of Public Safety and placed in charge of the State Patrol and Bureau of Investigation. Following this position he was appointed commander of Georgia's first Department of Homeland Security. He finished his long and illustrious law enforcement career in 2003. In June 2012, in the presence of Georgia's top dignitaries, Robert Hightower participated in the formal ceremony to dedicate and name the Cobb County Police Headquarters in his honor. A short month later, at age seventy-eight, he passed from this earth carrying the distinction as "The finest lawman to have ever walked through the state of Georgia."

APRIL 17, 1964

Midnight

It was a typical Thursday night at Walt Tonge's Diner, a late-night, ten-table eatery known on the west side simply as Walt's. Though two miles opposite Atlanta's Northeast Expressway, the area was considered Duluth. At this time of night the diner's neon Open sign cast a hopeless lure to the empty north-south lanes of Highway 23.

Thirty minutes later, in the early hours of Friday, April 17, Gwinnett County Police Officer Jerry Everett, driving with partner Ralph Davis riding shotgun, pulled their new Plymouth four-door patrol car into the deserted blacktop parking lot adjoining Walt's.

Ignoring alignment of the dedicated white-striped spaces, the cop car lawfully seized its usual parallel position in front of the diner's panoramic window, a must-have slot for effecting quick departure, but mostly for

Officer Everett to admire, from the vacant dining room's center table, his county-lettered cruiser, the latest in their fleet of four, parked under the bright outside spotlights. He regularly drove that beauty of authority to Jimmy Hambrick's Amoco service station—where he also moonlighted pumping gas—to perform his own wash and wax job. Finishing touches glamorized its chrome antennas and red bubble lenses.

Tonge allowed the two officers to run a weekly tab. Payday came every other Friday. Twice a month the officers squared up with the diner owner. "Set your clock by it," claimed Walt. Inside the diner, after consuming their dinner, Everett, in no hurry to resume what was usually a boring second half to a late-night shift, settled in for police-themed talk with Tonge.

Officer Davis, bored from hearing it all many times before, wandered outside, patiently waiting for Everett. Returning to the front seat of Patrol Car Twenty-nine, he powered on the squad car's dual radio system, one set to the county's frequency, the other to the State Patrol.

The night's crescent moon seemed a million miles further away outside the patrol car's window. This night had Davis again dreaming about home with his adoring wife Gertrude, about bathing off another day of sweat-drenched field work and being settled down with her on the porch bench in the cool night air, gentle words to say and hear. His faithful 1954 GMC pickup stood in silhouette against a backdrop of seven fresh-plowed acres. He'd promised her, "Only be a few more weeks and you'll just have to put up with me full time from then on."

Inside the diner, as their late pow-wowing ran through a full coffee pot, Everett withdrew from his front pants pocket a single-shot .22 caliber derringer he called "My Little Bug," bought just days before from Duluth Pawn.

"Hey, Walt, you ain't yet had a chance to meet this little fella, have you?" Everett pushed the loading lever forward, releasing the barrel latch. After removing the single bullet in its chamber, he handed the gun to Walt.

Bouncing the tiny pistol up and down in the palm of his hand, Walt snickered in sarcasm. "Won't a fly swatter do ya better?"

Everett raised one eyebrow as he pointed his finger at the derringer. "You don't wanna get caught on the wrong end of that little bastard."

The county frequency blared out an interruption to Ralph's dreams. "Twenty-nine, radio, you copy?"

Davis answered, "Yeah, radio, Twenty-nine, go ahead."

Radio operator Clyde Pruitt reported, "Twenty-Six needs assistance at eighty-five and one eleven, Suwanee."

Davis responded, "Twenty-nine, roger. Three-seventeen from Two-Three north, Eighty-Five Diner."

The quick exchange set into motion not only a hasty departure from Walt's, but was also the first of several critical mistakes Officer Jerry Everett would make that night.

Pruitt's relayed request came from Officer Leonard Bowen. He and Officer Jesse Gravitt, past their end-of-shift quitting time, were on the scene of a one-car fire shouldering the Northeast Expressway's Suwanee off-ramp. In a fateful appeal, Bowen asked Everett and Davis to come get Gravitt and take him to his nearby Duluth home, an often played-out courtesy between overlapping patrol units.

Davis' raring-to-go entrance back into the dining room informing Everett of the call, especially helping another officer, had both cops scrambling for a speedy departure. Everett quickly grabbed the derringer from Walt, put it back in his pocket, and took off out the diner's front door. Everett did not have the presence of mind to reload his pistol. Its bullet, plus another, remained pocketed, an innocent but pivotal oversight perhaps from the newness of carrying the little gun or his concern for Gravitt's well-being. He might as well have left his derringer at home.

The patrolmen began their four-mile trip to Officer Gravitt's location less than ten minutes away. Three miles farther east, a trio of car thieves turned onto a dark single lane of dirt named Arc Road.

After arriving at the car fire scene and engaging a few words of cop talk with Officer Bowen, Everett and Davis, with Gravitt in the patrol car's backseat, started on their way to Gravitt's home. Inside of thirty minutes Gravitt would have been sitting in his night clothes on his front porch with a Tampa Nugget in one hand and a shot of Canadian Club in the other, if not for Pruitt.

An impressive smattering of disbelievers verbally attacked Pruitt for years for what happened to "those officers" on "that dirt road." Although an authentic eyewitness had substantiated the information in a fair court trial, the events to this day and probably forever going forward would always linger as uncorroborated. Who was to blame? What exactly happened?

∽

1:30 AM

A. C. Mills was more than mildly unhappy with his dog, Count, a Weimaraner of adult age and temper. The dog gave a rowdy, alarming bark for cars driving on "His Road" and then parking up the hill from "His Yard."

"Boy just had himself sure enough in a fit."

Through his grimy bedroom window Mills saw the lights of two cars no farther than an eighth of a mile away on the single-lane dirt road. He also saw shadows of what seemed like maybe two or three men standing in the road. Turning to his wife, Ruby, he said, as he would angrily repeat minutes later over the phone to radio operator Pruitt, "They's lighting cigarettes and talking top of their voices. Ain't spose to be nobody out here this time of night."

Count began barking from the time the cars appeared, and Mills "couldn't get him hushed," not that Count was disturbing the neighbors; there weren't any neighbors on the desolate county road. Count, with his keen hearing and excellent night vision, was irritated. It mattered not the time of night or complaints of his master. All of which kept him and Ruby from "Gettin no sleep," according to Mills.

A call came over the county's frequency again. "Twenty-nine, radio, you copy?"

Officer Jerry Everett answered, "Copy."

"Twenty-nine, we got a disturbance call on Arc Road. Where you at?"

"Pleasant Hill and Eighty-Five, radio. Say again, call."

"Arc Road. Do you have a location?"

"We'll find it. Over."

Officer Everett had seen signage indicating the road whenever he'd driven by, but he had forgotten the exact location. When he told Pruitt "We'll find it," Everett remembered the road.

Humored by Mills' colorful phone language and afterwards the radio call to his only police motor unit in service, it seemed like a good time for Pruitt to close down his late jailhouse shift. Those last few simple words of radio talk with Jerry Everett would end all official communication for the night and Gwinnett Patrol car Twenty-nine was on its own.

Everett drove east on Pleasant Hill from the Northeast Expressway and turned right onto Arc Road where a single house sat on the left corner. Two hundred yards farther along another house sat on the right. A mile in, the road tapered to a one-car squeeze-through at its valley intersection with Bromolow Creek. An unsettled wooden bridge, originally built for a mule-driven hay wagon rather than a two-ton police car, connected the divided halves of Arc Road's span.

Boulders half the size of cotton bales, which prevented rising creek water from washing out the flimsy structure, lined both sides of the narrow passage. After a cautiously slow traverse over the bridge, the police car continued to a quick bend to the right and then a hundred feet further made a sharp bend back to the left. After this only deviation to its straightness, still on a flat plain, sat an old one-room wooden field house to the right, abandoned some time before and nearly rotted to the ground. The branches of a century-old oak tree covered the road's full width.

In a leisurely decline from a crest that put Beaver Ruin in sight, the home of A.C. and Ruby Mills tucked back a hundred feet off the road's left side, the only residence on Arc Road's entire southern half stretch.

∽

1:45 AM

Officers Davis, Everett, and Gravitt, in no particular rush and the road's derelict condition not allowing hurry anyway, made small talk for that first dark mile, discounting the call of disturbance. They had not found any yet. "Nobody drove on Arc Road at night." Not until they approached the narrow bridge over Bromolow Creek did they have cause for any concern, but late-night April dew looked thick as fog, combined with the mist rising from the creek. Worthless headlights blindly reflected off a veil of white haze.

Flashlights pointed out the car windows shone off the rickety bridge and then off its protective boulders. Finally, sixty feet farther, after the car broke through the worst of the fog, the headlights found their way. Everett drove through the swerves, sharply right and then sharply left.

He continued through Arc Road's valley as its flat bottom gave way to the steep hill ahead, but only after passing the old collapsed field house on his right. The slow ride up Arc Road's rutted south side returned a sense of serenity to the officers when, clear of all haze and mist, it revealed only a quiet country dirt road. The field on the left glowed from a magnificent bright moon captured within a web of sparkling stars. Crickets rejoiced loudly in numbers that overwhelmed the calm.

એન

THERE THEY WERE

Arc Road hill crested with flatness several car lengths long. Deep ruts directed the exact course of the car. Finally, on the road's highest point into the officers' night search, amber running lights begged attention one hundred yards out front.

The subject of their hunt. Two cars were parked on the left side almost in the middle of the road, one right behind the other.

"There they are!"

Inside the lead car, a 1963 Oldsmobile, Venson Eugene Williams crouched under the steering wheel to trade out the jimmied ignition switch for a keyed switch. From the passenger seat Alex S. Evans lit the activity with his flashlight. Stooped behind the rear bumper and directly in front of his 1962 Chevy, a third man, Wade Levi Truett, was midway through swapping the stolen car's rightful license plate for a bogus South Carolina dealer tag.

While Williams was making the swap, Evans removed the identifying car documents from the glove box and threw them out the passenger window. Truett was the first to notice the burst of patrol car Twenty-nine's high beams rising from behind the hill.

In an incorrect assumption that nobody would come driving down the deserted road, Truett had left his Impala's door wide open, blocking what little space there was to be had on the narrow road. After slinging the Oldsmobile's license plate into the field, he walked back to his car, but instead of just closing the door, he then sat behind the steering wheel and waited for the oncoming car to pass.

When Twenty-nine topped the hill, its headlights illuminated the Oldsmobile's interior with dazzling clarity, forcing the two men inside to retreat under the dash.

Everett activated the rotating roof beacon, the only patrol car in the county's fleet of four that had the latest two-way alternating beacon, one flash red, one flash white.

From the hilltop, challenged by no other light for a mile, the beacon lit the area back to Bromolow Creek and forward to Beaver Ruin Road, a jolt to the three evil intruders who had moments earlier freely rejoiced in a triumphant car heist.

Still scrunched underneath their temporary hiding place, Alex Evans was quick to identify officers Jerry Everett and Ralph Davis. He whispered to Williams, "I know these cops. You keep your mouth shut! Let me do the talking."

Twenty-nine, with its lights cutting through the dark, came to a stop in front of the Oldsmobile. Officer Everett stepped from the patrol car and stood in the road. Wade Truett turned scared rabbit. Truett cranked his Chevy engine, slammed the gear into reverse, and floored the gas pedal. A loud growl from the big-block motor followed by a squall of rocks and dirt made his chassis smash backwards down the rugged hill, a frantic 200-yard sidewinding drop smack into Count's world, A. C. Mills' gravel driveway.

Everett, not yet aware of the Oldsmobile's occupants, hollered to Davis, "Go get him!" Officer Gravitt remained in the backseat as Ralph slid behind the steering wheel, taking pursuit of the fleeing convertible. Everett stood alone in the dirt road, turning his attention to what appeared at first to be an empty automobile. He had little time to consider much. "Who was in that car squealing away? What is this car doing here?" His surroundings, except for the use of a tired flashlight he shook to revive, had returned to darkness.

He pulled on the Oldsmobile door handle and stepped back when it swung open. Pointing his flashlight inside the car interior, Everett was startled when he found two men sprawled across the front floorboard. He jumped back several feet, crouched down in the road, and drew his Smith & Wesson .38 revolver from its holster.

Cautiously he walked around the open car door, aiming his weapon at the mysterious men. Both wore white gloves. He shined his flashlight at each face. Nearest to him under the steering wheel was a man whose identity Everett did not know. Not so the man scrunched under the glove box.

"Well, I'll just be damned! Looky here what I found! That's you, ain't it Alex? Sure is. What's ya doing out here this time of night? Don't tell me. Let me guess. You and this boy here is stealing yourselves a car, ain't ya? Yeah, I believe that's exactly what y'all are doing. Nice one too, ain't it? Pretty little thing. Don't y'all care that somebody's gonna be missing this honey come morning? Get your damn asses out of there, the both of ya, right now!"

The two men sat up on the Olds bench seat then squirmed out of the open door. Williams stood first on the dirt road moving a few steps to the side, allowing Evans to follow.

Facing them, Everett commanded, "Turn around and lean against the car."

Doing as they were told, they propped themselves against the Oldsmobile's left quarter panel, Williams toward the back, Evans nearer to the middle, directly in front of Everett. The officer did not frisk his two suspects for weapons, nor would he be expected to.

Everett held his gun high, standing close to Williams, but stared hawk-eyed at Evans. "Who's your friend, Alex?" He did not wait for an answer. "Boy, don't you know hanging around ol' Alex here will get your ass in big trouble? Yes it will." He leaned close to Williams and whispered, "Just did."

Everett had little trust in Alex Evans. He had been with him plenty enough to know. In fact they patrolled together two years before when Evans was a Gwinnett County sheriff deputy. They trained together too, at FBI school in Atlanta. Officer Everett knew all about Evans then and more so now, with his criminal doings since his law enforcement downfall.

"Alex told you 'bout his Fed problems, has he?" The officer shined his light at Evans and back again at Williams. "What's your name, boy?"

Williams' answer was barely audible. Everett thought for a moment.

"Venson Williams, you say? Well hell! I know who you are. Damn, son! You're one of them got caught on that red-liquor heist, ain't ya? Mercy. You got Fed problems of your own. Seems like y'all just can't find yourselves enough trouble, huh? Well, you've sure found more tonight."

The officer shined his flashlight inside the Oldsmobile. The ignition switch dangled from underneath the dash. "Looks like I made it here not a minute too soon, didn't I, boys?"

Confident that the situation was in his control, Everett holstered his revolver as he leaned in through the door for a closer look at the switch. Whatever the officer was thinking, he thought wrong. Dead wrong. By letting his guard down, he committed the most grievous error a police officer can make in the field. He turned his back on a desperate and dangerous man waiting for an opportunity to gain the upper hand.

∽

Evans pulled out a snub nose .38 revolver hidden under his waistband and shoved the barrel against the middle of Everett's back. With his other hand he snatched the officer's gun from its holster. "Now Jerry, don't do anything stupid."

Everett instinctively threw an elbow square into Evans' chest, knocking him to the ground.

In the darkness Everett's outline loomed tall. For Evans, it was a target as he fell. He shot Everett in the back of his thigh. The bullet traveled upward, exiting two inches from his pants zipper. Grimacing, Everett applied pressure to the exit wound, smearing blood on the palm of his hand. He turned toward Evans and shouted, "You son-of-a-bitch! Assaulting a police officer with intent to murder! I'm gonna slam your ass in jail till you're an old man!"

Staggering several steps backward to regain his footing, Evans shouted in reply, "Damn it, Jerry, I told you not to do anything stupid. You should've listened. That was your own damn fault."

Venson Williams' mind was near panic. "God Almighty, what the hell just happened?" He never figured on any gunplay, but a bullet was fired, and "Oh goddamn! That son of a bitch Evans just shot a cop." After the bright flash of gunpowder in the dark, he was either a witness to this cop being shot or a party to this cop being shot, and whichever way he figured, he lost. "What was it he just told me? 'Boy, don't you know hanging around ol' Alex here will get your ass in big trouble?'"

I stole a car with the wrong dude. Evans is crazy. I've got to play this thing a whole lot different.

At the bottom of the hill, A. C. Mills stared through his bedroom window gasping in disbelief as Wade Truett's Chevrolet careened full-throttle backward and slid into his driveway, straight toward his house. All six of the low-slung Impala's rear lights glowed bright enough to light up his whole front yard and house before the car finally skidded to a stop just feet from his front door. Truett quickly shifted the transmission into Drive and stomped the gas pedal, but the carburetor flooded, and the big Chevy motor choked out.

Seconds later Officer Davis entered the driveway himself in a sideways slide. Twenty-nine's roof beacon flashed as the patrol car came to a ground-scrubbing halt. Headlights faced headlights between dust kicked up by the skid. The chase ended with the stalled Impala blocked against Mills' front porch.

Officer Gravitt stepped out of the patrol car's rear door. He pointed his flashlight at Truett and cautiously approached the Chevrolet. Baffled by the stranger's insane getaway attempt, unaware of either the Oldsmobile's theft or the gunshot fired in Everett's leg, he stood against the driver door and searched through the car interior with his flashlight.

He slanted a puzzled squint at the driver. "Boy, have you lost your damn mind?" He shook his head. "I don't believe I've ever seen anybody do that before."

Although suspicious of the driver's motive for fleeing, Gravitt did not draw his gun. "You must wanna go to jail real bad tonight." Officer Gravitt opened the car door and noticed Truett wearing white gloves. "Come out of there and let me sit you in the back of that patrol car till I figure out what's going on."

Afraid to say anything, Truett walked quietly with Officer Gravitt to the patrol car.

Still miffed, Gravitt asked, "What were you thinking? You could've killed yourself driving like that."

Davis stood outside the driver door while Gravitt helped Truett into the patrol car's backseat. He was not handcuffed. Gravitt closed the door and pointed at the Impala. "Ralph, hold up here for a minute. Let me see if I can't get that thing going."

The flooded motor sputtered to life and Davis backed his patrol car in a semicircle beside the house. Gravitt shifted the Impala into gear, and with Davis following, both cars drove out of Mills property. As they headed back up the hill on Arc Road to where the chase began, the poorly kept dirt road made their return sensibly slow.

Everett was relieved to see the cars coming back. He felt confident his partners would take control of the situation.

Evans also watched as the headlights slowly approached, still more than one hundred yards away. He made an attempt to win over the wounded policeman. "Look, Jerry, I can get us out of this mess if you'll just tell them the gun went off by accident. They'll believe it if you say so." Continuing to hold Everett at gunpoint he more urgently pleaded, "I've been thinking about this for a good while. You and me together, we can make some damn good money, the two of us. All you need do is work with me."

In spite of Everett's leg wound and overall predicament, the thought of any joint venture with Evans infuriated the hardened cop. "I'm gonna throw your sorry ass behind bars for a long time."

With his scheme not working Evans waged a tirade of indignation on the policeman. "You seem to be forgetting something here, boy! Who you're dealing with. It's me, Jerry. I'm making you a respectable offer, and you just shut me down. Maybe I need to remind you of something, Joyce and them three little babies of yours. Yeah! You're doing a real fine job providing for them all right! That bullshit county pay...scratching out a few dollars at that gas station...yeah, I bet you feel real proud of yourself about that, huh?"

Gritting his teeth, Everett growled, "You heard what I said. A long time means a long time."

With the two cars only moments away, Evans shrugged, held his gun low in front of his waist, sat down in the Oldsmobile seat, and berated Everett's refusal. "Shit, Jerry, you ain't nothing but a stupid fool." Evans slid over to the passenger side. "Okay, I tried to give you a break, but now I'll just have to go alone."

Everett felt the blood drip down his leg. "Only place you're going to is hell."

Evans waved the gun. "Get your ass in this damn car! Stick yourself under that dash and stay there! I swear if you so much as move your little finger, I'll blow your brains out."

Officer Gravitt parked behind the Oldsmobile. The Chevy headlights found Venson Williams leaning against the left rear fender, and he too was wearing white gloves. Everett laid half out the open driver door. He shut down the Chevy motor, turned off the headlights, and stepped out onto the road. Officer Davis pulled up close behind, turned off the ignition, but left the patrol car headlights on. The three cars were in a straight line only a few feet apart. Davis removed Truett from the patrol car's backseat, and both men walked to the front of the Chevrolet. Officer Gravitt stood in the road shining his flashlight toward Williams' face. Although the Chevrolet convertible in front was blocking the patrol car's headlights from behind, Truett later explained, "There wasn't all that much light, but enough to where you could make out what was going on."

Out of view inside the Oldsmobile Evans was balled up against the closed passenger door. Having been caught stealing a car, shooting a cop, and holding him hostage, there was no turning back. The deal had gone down, and the consequences of attempted murder would land him in jail, as Everett declared, for a long time, a duration he had no intention of serving.

Everett knew his partners were walking into a trap, but with his own gun held against him by a crazed felon with an itchy trigger finger, he couldn't alert them. He remembered the pocketed derringer, bought for just such a situation. In the dark he could quickly slide it out, stick the .22 caliber barrel in Evans' ear, and slam the hammer down, ending the issue. Would, he realized, if only he'd reloaded it at Walt's diner. That first mistake of the night, along with letting his guard down ten minutes earlier, had put all their lives in peril.

For Davis and Gravitt the scene presented a less threatening encounter. With Everett lying on his side across the driver seat shining his flashlight under the dash and these two road hustlers clad in white-gloved-guilt, they seemed to have simply stumbled upon car thieves in the act. A little unusual to catch them red-handed but not surprising for this part of the county.

The four men stood huddled on the dirt road within arm's length of one another. Williams stood with his back to the Oldsmobile. Truett, arms folded, leaned against the Chevrolet hood. Davis and Gravitt stood between them, facing the Oldsmobile.

Despite appearances, even if void of criminal conduct, Williams was caught in a quandary by the officers' calm manner. *Those two cops got no clue the big one sitting there's been shot. Wade don't neither. Got no idea Alex is holding a gun on him. With this mess already, hell, there ain't no telling what he might do next. Crazy bastard's got enough firepower to spring out and waste all five of us.*

Williams had brought his gun from Hartsville that morning, Truett too, but both weapons were tucked out of sight under the Chevy's front seat. Though he could not afford any more gun charges against him, Williams wished "the damn thing" was tucked inside his waistband.

While Gravitt's flashlight and attention were focused on his ID, Williams nodded at Truett. Waving with his eyes, he indicated the Oldsmobile's open door. Truett took the gesture as meaning some type of scheme was in the works. Stalling for time he began fumbling inside his wallet for a torn-in-two Georgia chauffeur's license, half of which he'd already handed Officer Davis. As Truett held the open wallet down below his waist he distracted Davis by asking, "Officer, could you please shine your flashlight here?"

Jerry Everett sat up straight in the Oldsmobile. He swung his legs out onto the road and exited the car, leaving the driver's seat covered in blood. His hands were not raised and he showed no sign of past or impending trouble. Evans closely followed, shadowing behind the tall cop. Both stood on the road, just outside the car door, only steps away from the tight circle of men. Still focused on their IDs, the officers didn't notice Evans' sudden appearance until it was too late. In the span of a moment Evans caught the two policemen off guard. "Get your hands up!"

Through the dim light Truett saw Evans pointing what appeared to be a long-barreled police revolver at Everett's head. Held high in his other hand was the .38 snub-nose revolver he'd seen inside Evan's waistband earlier that evening.

Officer Gravitt reached for his own gun, but Evans cocked the hammer on both revolvers and shouted, "If you pull that pistol, I'll blow your damn brains out."

Officer Everett hollered, "Don't do it! He means it!"

Gravitt moved his hand away as Evans coaxed in approval, "That's it, nice and easy. Venson, take their guns." As Davis and Gravitt stood in the road with their hands up Williams walked behind them, pulling their guns from their holsters. He shoved one in his pants pocket. The other he held in his hand.

Evans pointed the police gun at Williams. "No you don't, Slim! Hand 'em over." He cautioned, "Slow and easy now, one at a time." Evans took the guns and tucked them into his belt, an act of his supremacy, a position he did not relinquish and Williams did not challenge.

Officer Davis tried to instill some logic that had escaped his friend, "Alex, do you have any idea what you're getting yourself into? Man, this ain't no game! I mean to tell ya this thing is fixing to get a whole lot worse than you can imagine."

"Why are you doing this, Mr. Evans?" Gravitt too criticized his captor's judgment. "You best be thinking real hard 'bout what you're doing, 'cause you're getting in a heap of trouble you can't get out of. I'd stop all this if I was you!"

"Shut up! Everybody just shut the hell up!"

Truett recalled he was surprised at the conversation between Evans and the officers. With their exchange of names, especially first names, he figured correctly that Evans and the officers knew each other, a fact Truett could not have known unless he was with Evans at the crime scene. That fact—that he had met Truett—was one Evans perpetually denied during his sworn testimony and through the many years of subsequent hearings in front of Georgia's Parole Board.

Evans stepped several feet into the road's dark fringe. He stood separate from the group. Both his revolvers had clear range on all five men. In his right hand he angled the large police revolver toward the car and then pointed it directly at Truett. In a hurried voice he ordered, "Venson, have your partner here handcuff 'em all together." Intently poised behind the drawn .38s he watched steel-eyed as Truett removed the handcuffs from Davis' and Everett's belt cases. Truett pulled the policemen close together in a small triangle, tightly grabbing hold of each officer's hand while fidgeting with the unfamiliar metal rings. His hands shook. He unfolded the first pair and then clamped Davis' left wrist to Gravitt's right. With the second pair he clamped one cuff around Everett's right wrist and the other cuff to the first pair's connecting chain.

Led by impulse, Williams separated himself from the group. He walked behind the Chevrolet to the police car, opened the door, and sat down in the driver seat. He'd been up for more than twenty hours, driving all day and night, drinking beer, stealing a car, witnessing a cop get shot, and now, of all things unbelievable, party to the unlawful restraint of three police officers. It had become a screwed-up bungle of escalating criminality that had begun as a routine car heist.

"Goddamn Evans! Son of a bitch has got me in an A-one mess if ever the hell I've been." His mind argued, "Maybe I'll just crank this thing up. Split out like a spooked cat in the night. Or maybe the cops got more guns in here. Grab me one and come out blasting."

But he couldn't drive away. Not in a police car. "With all those State boys out this time of night I'm sure to get caught." And if he found a gun he would not shoot anybody. That was never a part of his illicit side. His best course was self-preservation, to act like a willing participant. He ripped through the headliner and tore out the wires of the patrol car's dome light. With a quick yank, he ripped out the two radio microphones, tossing them across the front passenger seat.

Acting the cool tough guy, Williams strode back to the group. "I took care of that cop car." He looked at Evans and then pointed at the policemen. "So what do ya think we ought to do with 'em?"

Still suspicious of his partner, Evans answered the question with one of his own, "I don't know. How 'bout you tell me."

Williams declared, "When they put those uniforms on they automatically become S.O.B.s right then. I don't give a damn what we do with 'em. It makes no difference with me."

Evans glared at Truett. "Okay, and you? What do you think we should do with 'em?"

Truett nervously steadied himself with a deep breath. "I'm thinking maybe we should tie 'em to a tree somewheres up in these woods. Somewheres out of sight. They'll be all right till morning. Let's just take the hot car and beat it. Won't be more than an hour, hour and a half, till we're over the Carolina line. By the time their found, we'll be long gone."

Evans scoffed. "Yeah, right." He knew that by mid-morning sheriff deputies would knock down his door with an arrest warrant.

Evans shined his flashlight at the Oldsmobile's open door, "All right, Slim, put 'em in the backseat. We'll take 'em on over the hill. I know where there's thick woods. We'll tie 'em to a tree can't nobody see from the road."

As Williams maneuvered the policemen toward the Oldsmobile, Evans noticed the blackjack each officer had sheathed on his belt. "Whoa, hold up right there." He stepped around Williams and took their clubs. "You won't be needing these anymore." He tossed them over the Oldsmobile's roof, where they fell within feet of where he'd thrown the car documents. Then he nodded at Williams. "All right, get 'em in."

Williams wedged himself between the driver door and the three cuffed officers. He reached inside the interior, released the front seat forward, and then stepped aside as they awkwardly crawled in through the driver door, Davis first, Gravitt in the middle, and Everett last, his hand across Gravitt's chest. They had to wriggle their shoulders up and down to slide across the wide backseat. When the men were finally in place, Everett's cuffed right hand rested pinned against the seatback behind Gravitt and Davis. Williams returned the driver seat to its upright position, finding the blood stain from Everett's leg wound.

Evans pointed at a tree-lined path ending sixty feet farther into the woods. "Venson, have your partner here get that cop car off this road. Hide it back in between those trees, then follow us."

Williams said, "All right, sure, but Wade's car is in the way."

Watching Truett slip into his Impala, Evans couldn't help thinking about Truett's foolish attempt at fleeing earlier and the very real possibility he would try it again. He shouted out, "Hey, wait up just a second! You and me need to talk."

Evans casually walked to the Chevy and leaned through the window, bracing his revolver atop the door ledge just under Truett's face. "After you get that car in there, you be sure to come follow us right quick, ya hear? Or else...." Evans raised his head from the window and gazed down the dark stretch of Truett's failed getaway route. He turned, facing back into the window, staring closer. He spoke through clenched teeth, "You try pulling that bullshit on me again, I'll track your punk ass down,

and I swear on a stack of goddamn Bibles, I'll kill you."
He turned to leave but stared back at Truett. "Believe it."

"Yeah, sure Alex! Take me a minute to move these cars, and I'll be right there."

Sitting behind the steering wheel, Truett cranked the Chevy engine. Evans stepped around the backside of the Oldsmobile, opened the passenger door, and shouted to Williams, "Let's go, get in; you're driving."

Holding the long-barrel revolver flush against his chest, Evans sat down sideways in the front seat and then turned, aiming the gun toward the officers. Williams was hesitant to get in the Oldsmobile as he stared at the driver seat covered in Officer Everett's blood, but the revolver in Evans' hand said, "Do what I say." Williams slid in behind the steering wheel, smearing his clothes in the indisputable evidence. He cranked the Oldsmobile motor and then shifted into drive.

"Ain't no chance in hell we're getting away with this. They gonna keep hunting till catching or killing us!" He asked himself, "Do I go or do I tell this crazy son of a bitch sitting next to me I ain't having no more of this?" But one quick look at that loaded .38 pointed at him settled the issues.

Williams let off the brake and lightly pressed the gas pedal. The car began a slow drive up Arc Road.

Close behind the Oldsmobile by one hundred feet Truett stopped his Impala. He watched the stolen car's taillights slowly continue and then disappear over the hill. He thought, "Now's the perfect time to get the hell outta here. Ain't nobody watching. Those cops ain't gonna come after me again, that's for sure. And that crazy Evans...hell, he don't scare me. I'll do as I please 'cause I'm legit. Car too. Got papers to prove it. Ain't nobody keeping me. I'll be gone slick as night."

As he mulled a getaway plan the empty hilltop conveyed Evans' threat, "You be sure to follow right quicklike, or else."

Down the hill he saw the faint glimmer of moonlit chrome accenting the patrol car's front end. Most unsettling, on its roofline, the glass bubble of authority he saw rotating in A. C. Mills' driveway barely twenty minutes before. Like Williams, Truett did as Evans told him. He shifted his Impala into drive and pulled ahead, clearing his car from the entrance to the path where Evans had pointed.

He parked his Chevy then ran back to the patrol car on Arc Road. Truett slid behind the steering wheel and held the clutch pedal down with his left foot while pumping the gas with his right. He turned the ignition key, spinning the Plymouth's six-cylinder engine several times until it revved to life.

☙

Williams held his foot firmly on the brake pedal as the weighted Oldsmobile descended Arc Road's steep hill. The slow drive escalated the night's felony.

Officer Everett knew he was going to die. His leg wound, left unattended, would bleed out long before morning, but in law enforcement, partners' safety came first.

"How the hell did I get them in this mess?" He stared at Evans and thought, "That bastard ain't gonna set us out in the woods tied to a tree and leave like there's nothing happened. Sorry, little chicken ass is gonna kill us."

Though restricted in movement and badly wounded, Jerry Everett reached forward and wrapped his free left arm around Williams' neck. With his feet braced on the floorboard he pulled Williams over the driver seat with a twisting motion intent on breaking the felon's neck. Williams kicked and grabbed at the steering wheel, then the first deafening gun blast ripped through the car interior. The bullet entered Everett's right shoulder, crossed through his chest, and stopped just under the left collar bone. Williams' upper body stretched over the driver's seatback, his neck still clutched inside Everett's folded arm.

Jerry rolled his head to the right, staring open-mouthed in silence at his old friend. Evans steadied the police revolver above his front seat, extended the gun one foot closer toward Everett, and fired a second time, point blank. The blast was twice as deafening and the gun smoke billowed twice as thick through the interior. The bullet tore through Officer Everett's upper gum, destroying the top portion of his mouth. The slug penetrated and shattered his brain stem before finally stopping just under the skin in the back of his neck.

The officer's upper body slumped against the side of the car. Williams reached for the steering wheel and pulled free from the policeman's grasp. Evans again leveled the pistol above his front seat and fired a third time. The bullet struck Everett above his right ear and traveled down through his skull before tearing out a jagged section of his cheekbone on exit. In five seconds, firing three shots from the officer's own gun, Alex Evans had murdered his one-time close friend, Gwinnett County Police Officer Jerry Everett.

Venson Williams, laboring to breathe, shoved the gear into park, opened the door, rolled out into the roadside ditch, and squatted in the soft dirt. He placed both hands around his stretched and twisted neck. Although his upper body wrenched in pain, Williams only thought, "Goddamn him! He just killed that cop! That bastard son of a bitch just killed that cop!"

A half-mile away on the opposite side of the hill on Arc Road, Truett shifted car Twenty-nine into first gear. He drove forward, close behind the rear of his parked Chevy, and then shifted into reverse. While backing the car up the narrow path, Truett did not hear the gunfire inside the Oldsmobile. He jumped out from the parked car, threw the ignition keys into the woods, and then stumbled blindly through the dark, running back down to the road.

Evans got out of the Oldsmobile and stood in the road. Scowling at the body of Officer Everett slumped in the rear seat, he shouted at the other two policemen, "Get him out. Get him out of there right now!"

Startled, the officers squinted, unresponsive to Evans' command. He leaned in through the door and shouted maniacally, "I told you to get him out of here right now. Drag him out! Right now, goddamn it! Drag him out of there right now!"

The vile directive was easier said than done, considering the car's tilted position in the ditch and the officers' cuffed hands. On his own, Officer Davis could partially step backwards out the door, but Gravitt had to turn full circle to his right for both to exit. They reached back inside and grabbed Officer Everett by his right arm. Struggling, they began pulling Jerry's lifeless body head-first through the passenger door. After they made several attempts, his upper torso came out of the car. With one last tug, he dropped face down onto the road. The impact scuffed a two-inch abrasion on his forehead.

Davis and Gravitt crouched over the murdered policeman. Everett's cuffed right arm, although pulled straight behind his shoulder, allowed them little freedom to stand.

A quick flashlight scan by Evans revealed a narrow two-track path coursing alongside the crumbled field shack. The gullied path sloped uphill not more than forty feet before meeting thick woods.

"Pick him up! Get him off this road!" Outraged, he snapped, "Let's go, damn it. Move!"

Though Arc Road was seldom traveled, which is why Evans chose it, there was the possibility that a car might've come. That happenstance, of sudden unsuspecting help appearing out of the dark, was the officers' only hope of living through the night. Considering their emotions and Officer Everett's mass a struggle to move, let alone carry, Evans could shout all he wanted. The two remaining officers were in no hurry.

Infuriated by the policemen's hopeless attempts, Evans yelled across the Oldsmobile hood, "Venson, get over here!"

Likewise in shock and physically spent, Williams shook himself upright and staggered around the front of the Oldsmobile.

"Grab around his legs and get him off this road. Move, damnit, move!"

With Everett's body lying between them, Officer Davis placed his free hand under Everett's armpit. Gravitt placed his free hand under Everett's other arm. Their cuffed hands grabbed the back of his belt and lifted his upper body off the road. Williams stood between Everett's legs, wrapped his arms around his knees, and lifted the officer's lower body. After a wobbly start they managed to carry him slowly around the back of the Olds.

Evans followed close behind, lighting their way with his flashlight as he directed them onto the washed-out trail. "Keep going till we get to those trees. I'll tell you where."

After a forty-foot trudge of jostling for balance, losing their grip, dropping, pausing, and then picking the body back off the ground, the men cleared the path and entered an area hidden from the road. Footfalls crunched pinecones and twigs as they continued. Musty odors from disturbed ground decay rose above their shuffling steps. Uneven boot and shoe imprints recorded the ghastly trek. One more pace, and Officer Davis' foot caught a briar vine. The nasty stickers sliced two horizontal scratches just below his left ankle. One more short and final entangled step tripped him. The others fell with him. He rolled over on his back, pausing to recover, his cuffed left arm extended over his face.

Gravitt kneeled. His cuffed right arm stretched to Davis' left. With Everett face down between them, his right hand contorted around the right side of his neck and connected to the cuffed hands of his partners. Their joined hands rested beside the murdered policeman's right shoulder. The exhausted men settled on the ground. Late night cricket calls added sound to their tired breathing.

Williams crawled to one knee and then pushed himself off the ground, still rubbing his hurt neck. He called to Evans, "Let's get the hell out of here!"

❧

Wade Truett ran to his waiting Chevy, jumped in behind the steering wheel, and shifted into gear. He anxiously drove up the unfamiliar dirt road. After topping the hill he peered down the dark road looking for the Oldsmobile, but the stolen car was parked much farther along in the valley, out of his view.

Officer Gravitt knelt and in a single motion removed the wallet from his back pocket and flung it through the trees.

Evans heard something tumbling in the woods, walked up behind the officer, leaned over him and asked, "What did you just throw?"

"A little over one hundred dollars. You want it, you go get it."

"I don't need to go get nothing from you!"

"Then you can go to hell, you son of a bitch!"

Evans' temper rose. He shoved the revolver muzzle against the policeman's right eye and pulled the trigger. The gun blast blew through Gravitt's skull and exited out the back.

Evans quickly stood, leaning over Officer Everett's body. He straightened his arm, aiming at Officer Davis' face at close range and pulled the trigger. The bullet entered the left corner of Officer Davis' mouth and blasted out several teeth from his upper jaw before plowing through and exiting the back of his neck.

All six rounds in the gun cylinder had been fired. Evans tucked the nickel-plated revolver under his belt buckle and then drew out the second police gun. Again he extended his arm, leaned over Everett, and from very close range, pulled the trigger as fast as he could, shooting Ralph Davis in the face four more times.

He stood, stepped a few feet to the left, leaned forward, extended the gun muzzle against Officer Gravitt's head, and pulled the trigger. The bullet entered the back of his head and exited his left temple. Evans continued holding the muzzle close and pulled the trigger again. The hammer struck the bullet primer, but the last live round in the gun cylinder failed to fire.

Evans quickly stood, tucked the pistol back under his waistband, and pulled out the third police revolver. He leaned forward and extended his arm again, holding the gun at close range. In rapid fire Evans shot Jesse Gravitt three more times in the back of his head. Still leaning forward, his arm still extended, Evans swept his gun hand slightly right, placed the muzzle against Officer Everett and pulled the trigger twice, shooting two more bullets into the back of his head. The last bullet he fired barely grazed Everett's face before plowing into the dirt underneath.

Truett, halfway down the backside of Arc Road's hill, heard the rapid gunfire. Nearing the flat valley he found the Oldsmobile parked with its left wheels settled inside the ditch. A mature oak tree hovered above the car, its long branches stretched across Arc Road's width. Truett parked behind the Oldsmobile and stepped out in the road. He jumped over the ditch and walked a few feet up a small bank. He saw the dim flicker of a handheld flashlight. He walked over the bank into the woods until, after several more steps, he could distinguish Evans from Williams. The men stood beside each other within a patchwork of thinning trees. Though Truett couldn't see the murdered officers, there was a faint but long-ago familiar gurgling sound.

He took another hesitant few steps forward. Just ahead, twenty feet away, deep blue uniforms lay blended together. Puzzled and scared stiff, Truett wondered, "Where are those three cops? I don't see any tree." A glancing wave from Evans' flashlight revealed contrasting spots on the ground. Peering closer Truett made the spots out to be white socks above shoe bottoms. "Oh, they killed 'em! Son of a bitch! Nobody said nothing about killing."

The gurgling noise became more pronounced. Officer Davis' lungs deflated slowly, gushing blood into his throat. The awful sound continued as his last breath cleared the bullet-shattered passageway. Concerned his marksmanship had not finished the officer, Evans drew the gun behind his belt buckle, flipped the cylinder open, and dumped the spent cartridges into his hand. He slid the casings into his pants pocket and handed the gun to Williams. Pointing his flashlight at the back of Jerry Everett's gun belt, he told Williams, "Load a couple of those bullets in that gun and shoot this one again."

Williams, as told, loaded two bullets in the revolver, placed the gun muzzle under Davis' nose, pointed the barrel upward and rapidly fired both rounds.

The bullets tore through the underside of Davis' face and exited the top of his skull.

The gurgling stopped.

Truett cringed at the sight of the gun blasts. He feared there'd be another victim. Him. Evans had already made the threat, and his buddy Williams had said, "I don't give a damn what we do with 'em." Maybe he wasn't as close a buddy as he was a short time before. "Goddamn Venson just shot that poor cop." Truett's fear was real and growing.

Seeing Truett standing nearby, Evans and Williams double-stepped out from the woods, walking straight toward him. Truett, figuring himself a witness to murder, ducked through the ditch and jumped behind the steering wheel of his Impala. Underneath the driver seat lay his loaded .38 revolver. He grabbed the weapon, placed it behind his waist, and concealed it under the tail of his sport shirt.

Evans scanned the Oldsmobile with his flashlight. He examined the car wheels then leaned through the open driver door. The interior reeked of gun smoke. Human blood and brain matter covered the window, the side panel, and the full length of the backseat.

Evans looked at Williams. "It's the only choice we got. I'm gonna drive this thing down the way. Tell your buddy to turn his car around, get ready to move." Evans gingerly slid in behind the steering wheel. The car wheels scrubbed free from the ditch. "Follow me; we're gonna light this damn thing a fire."

After he told Truett to ready the Chevy Impala for getaway, Williams ran down Arc Road to where Evans had wedged the Oldsmobile inside a stand of small trees.

The ditches bordering Arc Road were not easily judged in the dark, and Truett's attempt at U-turning his long convertible failed. The front wheels slid down into the gully and the car frame bottomed out, leaving him stuck under the big oak.

Evans stepped out of the Oldsmobile and stood clear. Williams leaned through the door, crouched under the steering wheel, and rolled the rubber floor mat halfway over. He threw a lit match under the mat, and the stolen car's floorboard slowly ignited.

The two men ran back to what they hoped would be a ready-to-go getaway car, but instead found the Chevy's front end hung over the ditch. Williams screamed through the driver window, "You stupid idiot! Hand me the keys."

Williams opened the trunk, removed the bumper jack, put it under the bumper, raised the back end of the car then shouted to his partner, "Floor the son of a bitch when I tell you." As he and Evans pushed on the raised car, Williams shouted, "Now!" The spinning rear wheels grabbed the hard clay and the Impala jumped clear of the ditch. With the car turned straight, Evans climbed into the front passenger seat. Williams hurriedly threw the jack inside the trunk, slammed the lid closed and walked around to the driver door. He told Truett, "I'm driving! Get your ass in the back."

As Truett climbed into the backseat, Evans saw the revolver tucked inside Truett's pants. Playing ignorant

Evans watched Truett's clumsy effort to move the gun between his legs and cover it with a pillow cushion.

The killers' urgency to leave heightened when the stolen car, fully ablaze, lit up the valley like a thousand angry torches. Swirls of white fire blasted through the side windows. Front and rear windshields imploded into an avalanche of scorched fragments. All four tires burst in rapid pops. The gas tank blew, hurling reddish-orange metal shards. With one final whoosh of flames and heat, the car rose slightly, the electrical harness melted, and the horn sounded a fatal scream before it too died.

Williams punched the gas pedal. Squealing tires kicked up a plume of dirt. The Impala's big motor roared through the late night as the car careened and squirreled, topping the hill on Arc Road.

Meanwhile, A. C. said to Ruby Mills, relieved, "Good! There goes that patrol car doing ninety miles an hour. Must be everything is all right. Maybe now we can finally get some sleep."

Williams skidded the Chevy heading up Beaver Ruin Road. He stomped down on the gas pedal hard. Evans, concerned that state troopers on post would not react too kindly of Williams' speed or his holdings, ditched the guns and flashlight over a quarter-mile stretch.

Count wildly paced his front yard. He stared at his land, across, up, and down. He pointed his nose high, sniffing the wind, his keen canine senses on alert. Count looked skyward to the moon, stars, and farther. He understood. He saw it clearly. He raised his head to the heavens and moaned for those soon to grieve.

ABOUT THE AUTHOR

Tony Tiffin is a Georgia native who, like many authors, has worked in many fields, from kitchen pearl diving to corporate aircraft sales. Now retired, his interest in the story of Arc Road began as a fifty-year-old captive memory. Researching this book became a ten-year journey that enriched his life with a renewed appreciation for Deep South traditions, a collection of new friends, the experience of shared emotions, and a greater respect for the fine people of Gwinnett County, Georgia.

9 781947 521100